P9-BJO-553

BIOMES OF THE WORLD

VOLUME 7
Tropical Forests

MICHAEL ALLABY

GROLIER EDUCATIONAL

About This Set

BIOMES OF THE WORLD is a nine-volume set that describes all the major landscapes (biomes) that are found across the Earth. Biomes are large areas of the world where living conditions for plants and animals are broadly similar, so that the vegetation in these locations appears much the same. Each of the books in this set describes one or more of the main biomes: Volume 1: The Polar Regions (tundra, ice cap, and permanent ice); Volume 2: Deserts (desert and semidesert); Volume 3: Oceans (oceans and islands); Volume 4: Wetlands (lakes, rivers, marshes, and estuaries); Volume 5: Mountains (mountain and highland); Volume 6: Temperate Forests (boreal coniferous forest or taiga, coastal coniferous forest, broad-leaf and mixed forest, Mediterranean forest and scrub); **Volume 7: Tropical Forests** (rain forest and monsoon forest); Volume 8: Temperate Grasslands (prairie, steppe, and pampas); Volume 9: Tropical Grasslands (savanna).

The books each have three sections. The first describes the geographical location of the biome, its climate, and other physical features that make it the way it is. The second section describes the plants and animals that inhabit the biome and the ways in which they react to each other. The final section of each book deals with the threats to the biome and what is being done to reduce these. An introduction in Volume 1 includes a map showing all the biomes described in this set, and a map showing all the countries of the world.

Throughout the pages of this set there are diagrams explaining the processes described in the text, artwork depictions of animals and plants, diagrams showing ecosystems, and tables. The many color photographs bring each biome to life. At the end of each book there is a glossary explaining the meaning of technical words used, a list of other sources of reference (books and websites), followed by an index to all the volumes in the set.

Published 1999 by Grolier Educational, Danbury, CT 06816

This edition published exclusively for the school and library market

Planned and produced by Andromeda Oxford Limited, 11–13 The Vineyard, Abingdon, Oxon OX14 3PX, UK

Project Manager: *Graham Bateman*
Editors: *Jo Newson, Penelope Isaac*
Art Editor and Designer: *Steve McCurdy*
Cartography: *Richard Watts, Tim Williams*
Editorial Assistant: *Marian Dreier*
Picture Manager: *Claire Turner*
Production: *Nicolette Colborne*

Origination by Expo Holdings Sdn Bhd, Malaysia
Printed in Hong Kong

Set ISBN 0-7172-9341-6
Volume 7 ISBN 0-7172-9348-3

Biomes of the world.
p. cm.
Includes indexes.
Contents: v. 1. Polar regions -- v. 2. Deserts -- v. 3. Oceans -- v. 4. Wetlands -- v. 5. Mountains -- v. 6. Temperate forests -- v. 7. Tropical forests -- v. 8. Temperate grassland -- v. 9. Tropical grassland.
Summary: In nine volumes, explores each of the earth's major ecological regions, defining important features, animals, and environmental issues.
ISBN 0-7172-9341-6 (hardcover : set : alk. paper). -- ISBN 0-7172-9348-3 (hardcover : vol. 7 : alk. paper)
1. Biotic communities--juvenile literature. 2. Life zones--Juvenile literature. 3. Ecology--Juvenile literature. [1. Biotic communities.] I. Grolier Educational (Firm)
QH541.14.B57 1999
577--dc21 98-37524
CIP
AC

Contents

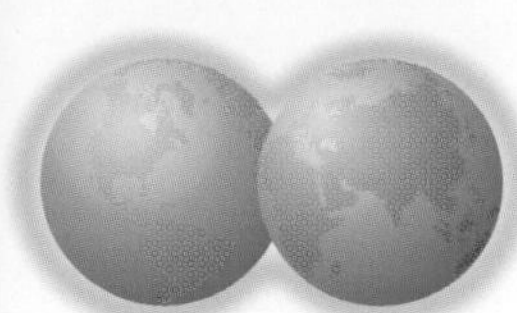

The Physical World of Tropical Forests

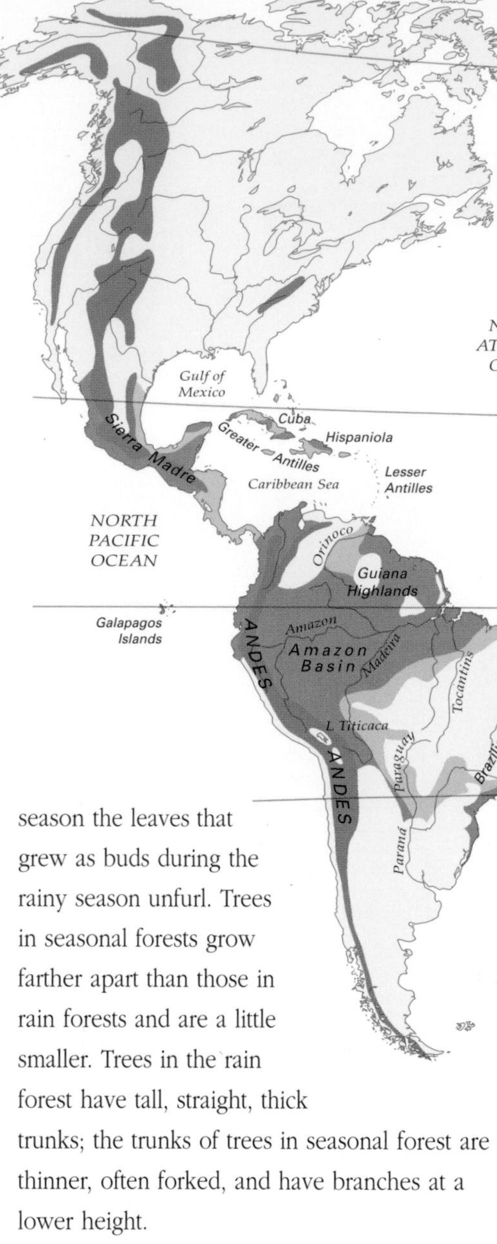

Giant trees towering to the sky and shading the ground; climbing plants entwined among the trees and hanging like ropes from boughs; brightly colored birds darting among the branches; the constant drip of rain: this is the popular vision of what a tropical forest is. But such an image is just part of a more complex picture.

There are several kinds of tropical forest, treated here within two biomes. The forest of tall trees and dripping rain—the forest many people envision when they think of "tropical" forest—is found in the lowlands, near the equator. There, where the rainfall is high and distributed fairly evenly throughout the year, the warm, humid climate produces the tropical rainforest biome.

In many parts of the equatorial region, however, the climate is variable, with clearly defined wet and dry seasons. This climate produces another biome: the seasonal tropical forests, the most typical being monsoon forest. Like rain forest, seasonal tropical forest is dominated by tall trees, but, unlike rainforest trees, they do not grow at the same rate throughout the year. They produce new stems and buds during the rainy season. As this season nears its end, this growth ceases. During the dry season the leaves that grew as buds during the rainy season unfurl. Trees in seasonal forests grow farther apart than those in rain forests and are a little smaller. Trees in the rain forest have tall, straight, thick trunks; the trunks of trees in seasonal forest are thinner, often forked, and have branches at a lower height.

Climates become more seasonal the farther away from the equator they are; reflecting this, forests also change the farther they are from the equator—they become more open, the trees smaller and more scattered. Gradually, tropical forest gives way to grassland. These forests, and the grasslands bordering them, lie in the tropics. This is the region between the equator and

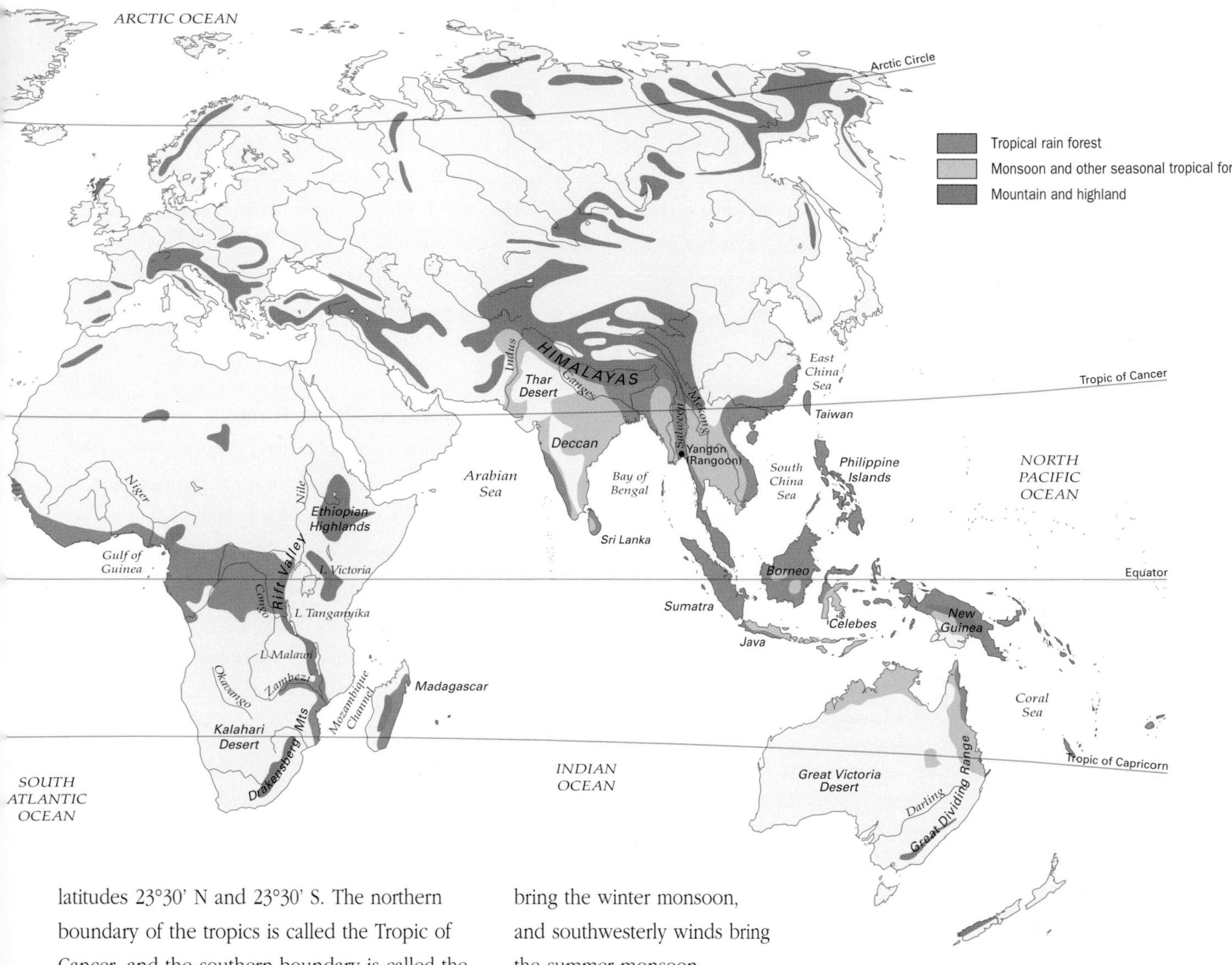

latitudes 23°30' N and 23°30' S. The northern boundary of the tropics is called the Tropic of Cancer, and the southern boundary is called the Tropic of Capricorn.

The contrast between dry and rainy seasons is most extreme in those parts of the world that experience the monsoons. The word monsoon comes from the Arabic *mawsim*, meaning "season." During winter high pressure over the continents produces dry winds that flow out from the land and over the sea. In summer pressure is lower over the land than over the sea, so the wind direction reverses, bringing air that is moist because it has crossed the ocean. Over the Indian subcontinent northeasterly winds bring the winter monsoon, and southwesterly winds bring the summer monsoon.

The winter monsoon is dry, and the summer monsoon is wet. At Yangon (Rangoon), Myanmar (Burma), for example, about 13 inches (330 mm) of rain falls between October and April. During the summer monsoon, from May to September, the rainfall is about 90 inches (2,290 mm). The Indian subcontinent and Southeast Asia have monsoon climates. Less extreme monsoon weather also occurs in parts of West Africa, Australia, and northeastern South America.

A dry season lasting for at least five months, along with a rainy season with intense rainfall,

TROPICAL FORESTS occur around the equator in Central and South America, Africa, eastern Madagascar, Asia, and the northern tip of Australia. These regions enjoy similar climates, but different species grow in their forests. In the tropics the lower slopes of mountains are often clothed in a type of rain forest.

LOWLAND RAIN FOREST appears *(opposite)* as a bewildering jumble of tall and smaller trees, climbing plants, and shrubs. These grow so closely together that the ground is shaded. Because the shade makes it difficult for small plants to grow, it is fairly open, so it is not difficult to walk through the forest. This forest is in the Democratic Republic of the Congo.

produces monsoon forest. This consists of fewer tree species than rain forest, and the trees are deciduous—they shed their leaves during the dry season. In many Asian monsoon forests sal (*Shorea robusta*) and teak (*Tectona grandis*) trees grow extensively.

INTO THE CLOUDS

Temperature decreases with height by an average 3.5°F every 1,000 feet (6.5°C per km). That is why there is a height above which trees cannot grow. It also means the type of forest changes several times between sea level and the tree line, above which the climate is too cold and windy for trees to grow. Forest extends to a considerable height in the tropics. The tree line is at about 13,000 feet (4,000 m) in the tropics (compared with about 8,000 feet [2,440 m] at latitudes 50° N and 50° S).

TROPICAL FORESTS

Continent	Total land area		Total forest area	
	'000 square miles	'000 ha	'000 square miles	'000 ha
Mainland Africa	8,407	2,177,367	1,883	487,767
Madagascar	224	58,154	57	14,889
Other islands	3	721	0.4	97
Total, tropical Africa	**8,634**	**2,236,242**	**1,940.4**	**502,753**
South Asia	1,592	412,297	239	61,836
Mainland Southeast Asia	734	190,125	262	67,877
Islands of Southeast Asia (Indonesia, Philippines, etc.)	944	244,417	487	126,038
Total, tropical Asia	**3,270**	**846,839**	**988**	**255,751**
Tropical Oceania	**209**	**54,055**	**161**	**41,752**
Tropical North and Central America	**1,022**	**264,801**	**309**	**79,958**
Tropical South America	**5,350**	**1,385,678**	**3,175**	**822,385**

(Source: Food and Agriculture Organization, United Nations)

Montane and Mossy Forest

Climbing from the lowland rain forest, the trees become smaller but have thicker trunks than those of the same species growing below them. Their leaves are smaller. These changes allow more light to penetrate, so there are more herbs growing near the ground.

This is mountain, or montane, forest. It contains fewer species of trees than lowland forest but has more ferns, mosses, and epiphytes. Epiphytes are plants, including some ferns, orchids, and bromeliads, that grow on the bark of trees. These plants benefit from the water brought to them in the moist air that is constantly rising up the side of the mountain.

With increasing altitude the air becomes still wetter. As the warm, moist air is forced to rise up the mountainside, it cools, and its water vapor condenses to form cloud. This covers the upper part of the mountains for most of the time. At ground level the cloud is a mist that covers everything. This produces cloud forest. It is also called mossy forest, because moss is everywhere. In places the ground is boggy and covered with bog moss (*Sphagnum* species). The trees are small, many of them gnarled, and they have tough, leathery leaves. Both trees and the ground are covered with mosses, ferns, liverworts, and flowering plants.

ANAMALAI SANCTUARY, in southern India, is an area of tropical rain forest among the hills of the Western Ghats, which run parallel to the Arabian Sea coast. Southern India and Sri Lanka were forested during the coldest part of the last ice age, so this forest may be very ancient.

In its upper parts the forest becomes more open, the trees become smaller, and there are even more ferns and epiphytes. This is sometimes called elfin woodland because of its strange, haunting appearance.

ANCIENT FORESTS

Coal is made from the partly decomposed remains of plants that once grew in tropical forests. Today coal is mined in the northern United States, northern Europe, and in China. There is even coal beneath the ice of Antarctica. Coal is found far from the equator because the coalfields of today once lay in the tropics, but they were gradually carried away from the region by the slow movement of the continents across the Earth, which is known as continental drift. About 400 million years ago North America lay at the equator. India crossed the equator about 60 million years ago.

Continents drift because the crust of the Earth consists of vast slabs of rock, called plates, that move in relation to each other. In some places, such as the center of the Atlantic, oceans are growing larger as new rock erupts from submarine volcanoes, pushing two plates apart. In others, in parts of the eastern Pacific for example, they are growing smaller as plates collide. Collisions cause one plate to sink beneath the other, one or both plates to crumple (forming mountain chains), or some combination of the two. Elsewhere (such as along the Pacific coast of North America), plates are moving past each other in opposite directions. The irregular, jerky motion of the plates causes earthquakes.

For about the last 200 million years what are now tropical South America and Africa have not strayed from the tropics, although they have drifted away from each other. Southern Asia has been tropical for about 120 million years. Apart from India, tropical regions have not changed latitude in the last 200 million years or so. The lands that are now covered by tropical forest have therefore been in the tropics for a very long time. This suggests the tropical forests themselves may be very ancient.

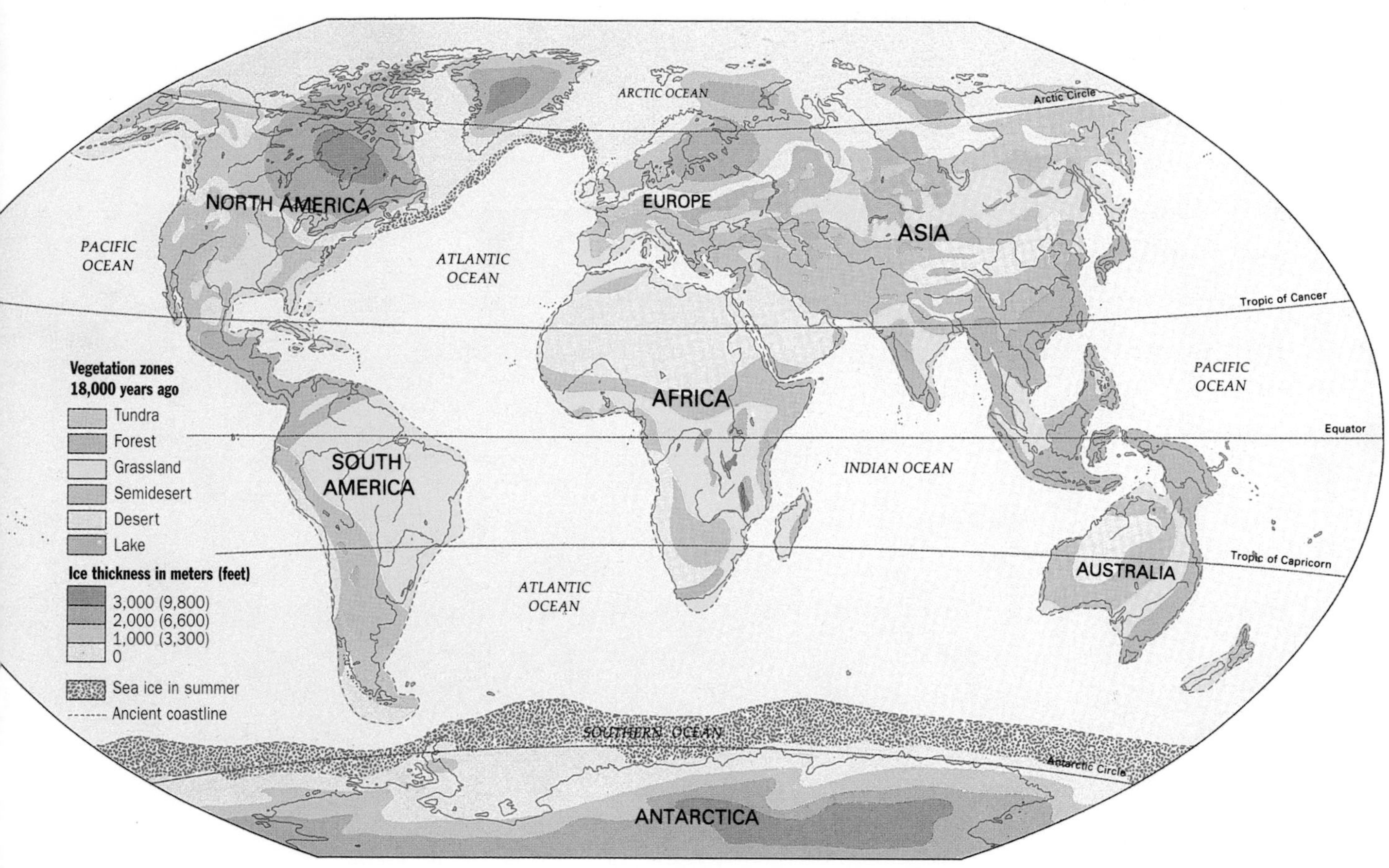

VEGETATION ZONES 18,000 YEARS AGO. During the coldest part of the last ice age, when the ice sheets reached their greatest extent, the tropical climate was cooler and drier than it is now, and most of the area now covered by tropical forests was grassland. In South America and Africa tropical forests survived in isolated patches, but they were more extensive in Central America and Asia.

The Evolution of Trees

The forests may be ancient, but they have not remained unchanged. Over so long a period this would be impossible because species evolve. Flowering plants, including broad-leaved trees as well as wild and garden flowers, first appeared about 130 million years ago. Prior to that forests consisted of trees related to firs and pines, together with tree ferns and other species that are now extinct. Tropical forests, like landscapes everywhere, would have looked very different from the way they look now.

Forests during Ice Ages

Although lands now lying in the tropics have been there for many millions of years, they have not always enjoyed the climates they experience now. Tropical climates, like climates everywhere, are constantly changing. The most dramatic change of climate is associated with ice ages.

In these periods great sheets of ice—a mile or more thick—spread south from the Arctic and covered part of North America, Europe, and Asia. The effect was much less in the Southern Hemisphere because there is less land. So much water was held in the ice sheets that sea levels fell throughout the world, and in many places coastlines extended beyond their present positions. Beyond the edges of the ice sheets the ground was frozen all year, and the vegetation resembled the tundra found today in the far north of Canada and Eurasia, and in Greenland.

There have been several ice ages. The most recent, which ended about 10,000 years ago, was

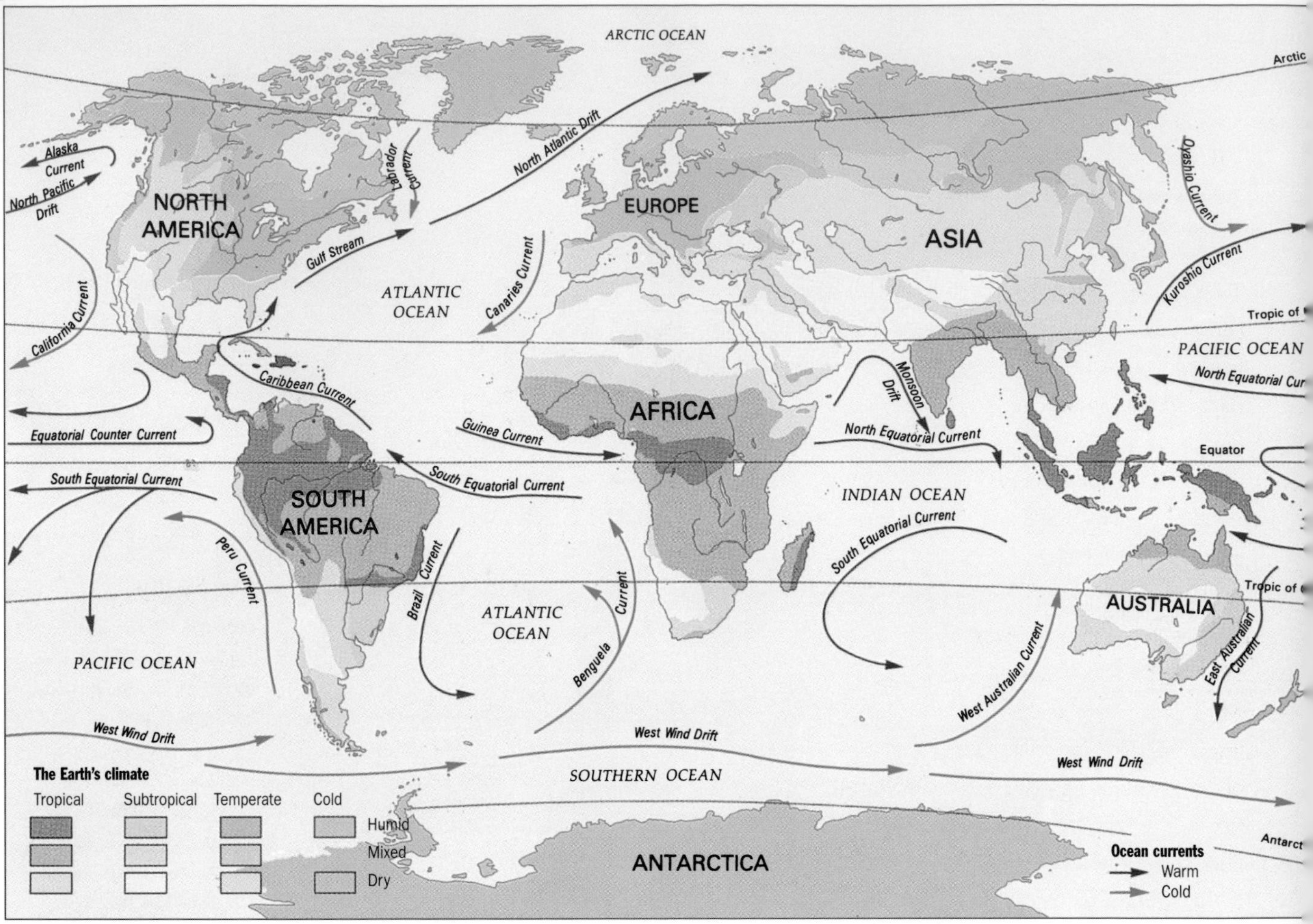

OCEAN CURRENTS AND WORLD CLIMATES. Ocean currents, driven by the wind, carry warm water away from the equator and cool water toward it. This circulation has a strong influence on climates. The map shows the principal warm and cold currents and types of climate.

at its coldest about 18,000 years ago. This is called the Last Glacial Maximum, and it is when the ice sheets reached their greatest extent.

When the weather is cold, less water evaporates, and so there is less rain and snow. In the tropics the climate during the last ice age was neither warm enough nor wet enough for the plants of rain forests to grow. In many places the forest was replaced by grassland. Grassland covered most of the South American tropics. Tropical forests survived, but mainly in the northwest of the continent and in Central America. In Africa tropical forests were reduced to isolated patches. In Asia the forests were more widespread.

As the climate grew warmer and wetter, tropical forests expanded into the grassland until eventually they covered the areas they occupy now. Later, forests also began expanding in the north, into land from which the ice sheets were retreating. Tropical forests expanded first, because they only needed a change in climate, whereas the northern forests could not expand until the ice had melted.

Asian tropical forest survived the last ice age. It is probably the most ancient forest in the world. The forests of South America and Africa are more recent. They are some thousands of years older than the forests of temperate regions, but that is all.

WHY THE WEATHER AT THE EQUATOR IS WARM AND WET

Today the equatorial regions have a warm, wet climate. The climate is warm because within the lines of latitude of the Tropics of Cancer and Capricorn the Sun is directly overhead at noon on at least one day every year. Outside the tropics the Sun is never directly overhead.

Imagine a flat disk with the Sun at its center and the Earth orbiting around its edge. The disk is called the plane of the ecliptic. The Earth is tilted on its axis, so it rotates at an angle of 23°30' in relation to the plane of the ecliptic, which is the same as the angle of latitude of the tropics. As the Earth moves around its orbit, first one tropical belt and then the other is tilted toward the Sun. This produces the seasons in both hemispheres.

Why It Rains

At all times of year sunlight is more intense in the tropics than it is anywhere else. The intense sunshine warms the surface of the land and sea, and the air is warmed by contact with the surface. Water evaporates into the warm air. The warmer air is, the more water vapor it can hold.

When air (or any gas) is warmed, it expands. Its molecules move farther apart, and this makes it less dense, because any given volume of it contains fewer molecules. Air above it is cooler and therefore denser, so the warm air rises. Over the equator air rises to a very great height because it is heated so strongly. Near the Earth's surface this produces a belt in which the pressure of the atmosphere at the surface of the Earth (atmospheric pressure) is usually low. As the air rises, it cools. This reduces the amount of water vapor it can hold, so the vapor starts condensing into droplets. These form clouds.

In the tropics clouds sometimes reach from a base below 1,000 feet (300 m) to more than 50,000 feet (15,000 m). The clouds produce rain; in most places close to the equator it rains on more than half the days in the year. The rain often falls as heavy showers or thunderstorms, and the Sun shines strongly between storms.

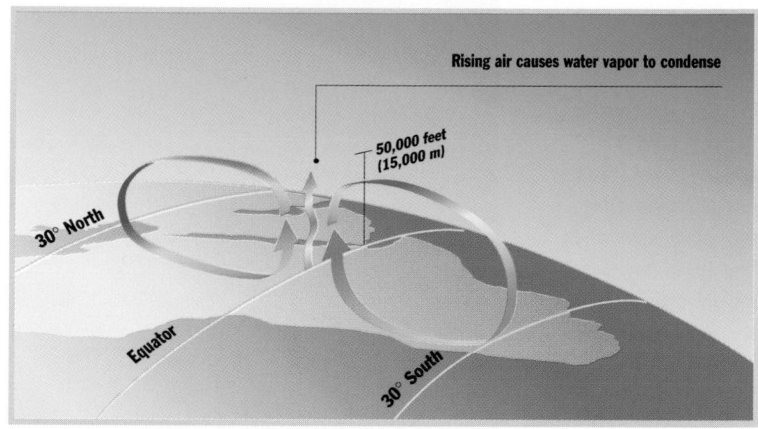

HADLEY CELL CIRCULATION. At the equator air is warmed by contact with the ground. Water evaporates into it. The air rises and cools, and its water vapor condenses to form clouds that release their moisture as rain. The air moves away from the equator, cools, sinks, and returns to the equator at a lower level.

George Hadley and Hadley Cells

Long ago, when merchant sailing ships traveled the world, sailors found that winds on either side of the equator were very reliable, almost always blowing from the northeast in the Northern Hemisphere and from the southeast in the Southern Hemisphere. These were named the "trade" winds, from the Old Saxon word for "track," because they blew in one direction.

Scientists sought explanations for why this was so. The English astronomer Edmund Halley (1656–1742) suggested in 1686 that air is heated at the equator, rises, and is replaced by cooler air

DEFORESTATION AND EROSION. At one time these hills, in Haiti, were forested. Clearing the forest to provide farmland increased the rate of erosion. The poor soils could not sustain the kind of farming practiced on them, and the land is now barren.

flowing toward the equator. George Hadley (1685–1768), an English meteorologist, improved on this idea. He suggested that the rotation of the Earth causes air flowing toward the equator to swing to the west, producing the northeasterly and southeasterly trade winds. The movement he described is still called a Hadley cell.

The air that is heated at the equator rises and moves away from the equator. By the time it reaches its maximum height, it is very cold and has lost almost all of its moisture. Still flowing away from the equator, it meets warmer air in middle latitudes and, because the cold air is more dense, starts sinking beneath it; at the same time it turns back toward the equator. As air sinks, it is compressed by the weight of air above it. Compression warms it. By the time the air reaches the Earth's surface, it is warm but still very dry. It then completes its circuit back to the equator as the trade winds. The belt in which the trade winds meet and air rises is called the Intertropical Convergence.

If the winds blow in the same direction for long enough, they can cause an ocean current to flow. Ocean currents carry warm water from the tropics toward the poles, and cold water from high latitudes back toward the equator. Because air is warmed and cooled by contact with the ocean, warm and cool ocean currents strongly influence the climates of continents close to them.

ROCKS AND SOILS

Soils form as rainwater dissolves some of the chemical compounds in rocks, and these react to release more compounds. Rocks eventually break into tiny particles. Plants use some of the released compounds, small animals feed on the plants, and the remains of plants and animals mix with the rock particles, then decompose.

The process of decomposition releases valuable compounds—plant nutrients—into water in the soil, from which plants can absorb them. Those not absorbed are carried downward by water: this movement is called illuviation.

Gradually, the soil develops distinct layers called horizons. Plant and animal debris lies at the surface, above decomposed organic material. Together these form the topsoil. In the subsoil beneath, illuviated compounds collect, and below that is a layer in which chemical reactions continue releasing compounds from rock particles. Below that is the "parent" rock from which the soil is made.

So nutrients are recycled, but with each recycling some of the nutrients are washed from the soil and carried into a river. Nutrients are replaced from the underlying rock, but, as the soil becomes deeper, the rock and its nutrients eventually lie below the reach of plants. The soil is old and increasingly infertile.

Tropical lands have the oldest soils in the world. Most of the plant nutrients sustaining the luxuriant vegetation of the tropical rain forests are held in the plants themselves. Decomposition is rapid, and plants take up nutrients almost as soon as they are released; the soils themselves contain few nutrients. In some places most chemical compounds have been lost from the soil, leaving behind iron and aluminum oxides and hydroxides. These form laterite—solid masses that can be hard as concrete and sometimes form an extensive layer. With care many tropical soils can be farmed, but lateritic soils are useless.

ULTISOL IS A TYPICAL SOIL OF THE HUMID TROPICS. Within it iron and aluminum compounds have been converted to their oxides, making the soil red or yellow in color. Plant nutrients have been washed away so the soil is infertile.

The Natural World of Tropical Forests

Driven by energy from the Sun and watered by the abundant rain, tropical forest trees grow to a massive size. Smaller trees grow in their shade, waiting for the giants to fall so they can reach for the sunlight. Animals feed on the plants that grow in the forest at all levels, from on and below the ground right up to the treetops.

Sunlight provides the energy for all plant life; because all animals obtain their energy from plants, every living organism in the forest derives its energy from the Sun. Even carnivores that never eat plants directly feed on plant-eating animals, or herbivores. Plants are able to capture energy from sunlight because cells in their leaves, and sometimes in their stems, contain tiny bodies called chloroplasts. Inside each chloroplast there are molecules of a substance called chlorophyll. The process by which energy is captured and stored in plants is known as photosynthesis.

Just below the protective outer layer of cells a leaf contains green tissue called mesophyll. This consists of rows of rather upright cells, a little like a fence or palisade, so they are called palisade cells. They are green because they contain chloroplasts, rich in chlorophyll, which is green.

The leaf also has small openings, called stomata (the singular is stoma), that can be held open or closed. When the stomata are open, carbon dioxide can enter the leaf. Water enters the roots of the plant and is carried to the leaves through specialized cells called xylem vessels. Water is needed for photosynthesis, but it also leaves as water vapor when the stomata are open.

When light strikes chlorophyll molecules, its energy is absorbed and drives a chain of chemical reactions. The first set of these reactions splits water into hydrogen and oxygen. The oxygen is released through the leaf stomata, and the hydrogen is used in the second set of reactions, in which hydrogen and carbon dioxide are combined with other substances already present in the chloroplasts.

The first set of reactions includes the absorption of light energy, so these are called the light reactions, or light-dependent reactions.

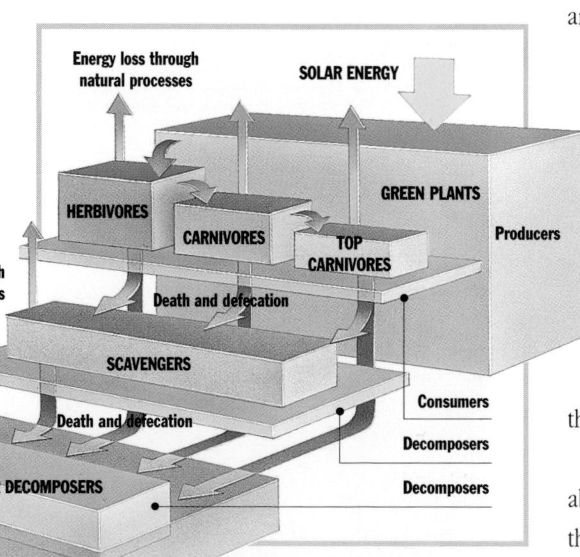

ENERGY FLOW THROUGH AN ECOSYSTEM. Green plants use energy from sunlight to make sugars. Plants and animals "burn" sugars to release the energy. Plant and animal wastes and dead tissues provide food for scavengers and finally for decomposers.

LEAVES are "factories" in which energy from sunlight is used to break down carbon dioxide and water, then to reassemble them in the form of sugars. This rainforest leaf *(left)* has a curved "drip" tip.

PHOTOSYNTHESIS *(below)* takes place in palisade cells, just below the surface of every green leaf. Water enters through the roots of the plant and is transported to the leaves by xylem vessels. Sugars are carried from the leaves to the rest of the plant by phloem vessels.

The second set of reactions uses chemical energy that has been passed on from the light reactions. They do not require direct sunlight and are called the dark reactions, or light-independent reactions. The second set of reactions was first described by Melvin Calvin, of the University of California at Berkeley in the United States, and are also known as the Calvin cycle. The cycle builds glyceraldehyde 3-phosphate, which is a sugar.

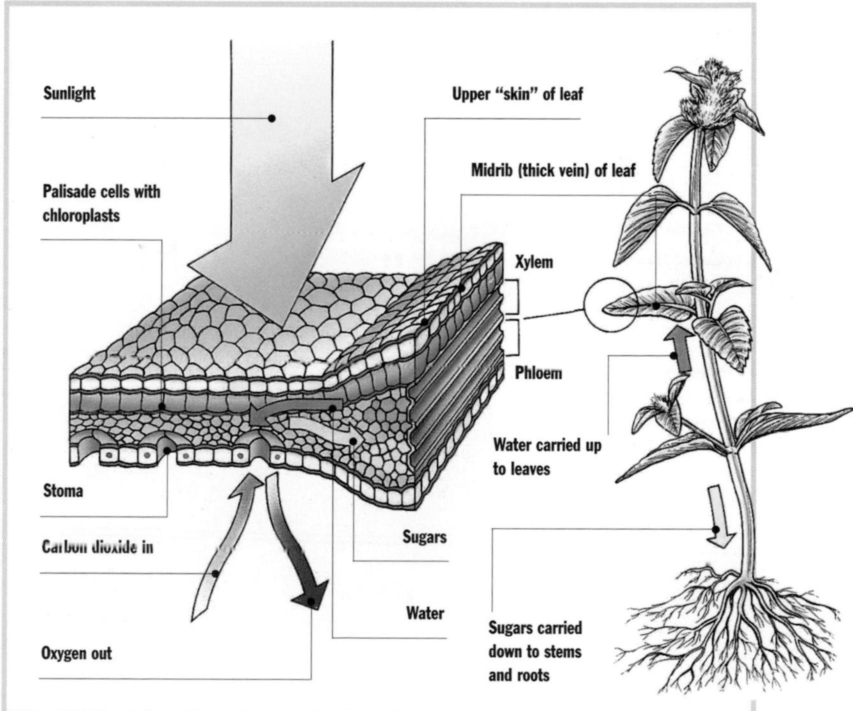

PRODUCERS AND CONSUMERS

Plants synthesize (manufacture) sugars. Oxygen is then combined in a process known as oxidation. The oxidation of sugars releases energy, and the chemical products are carbon

A TROPICAL FOREST ECOSYSTEM is complicated because of the large number of species it contains, but these are related to each other in the same way as in any ecosystem. Trees and other plants are the primary producers. Herbivorous birds, mammals, insects, and other invertebrates are primary consumers. Carnivorous amphibians, reptiles, birds, and mammals are secondary consumers. Scavengers include vultures as well as small soil-dwelling animals. This ecosystem is in South America.

Components of the ecosystem

1 Fruits and seeds
2 Epiphytic plants
3 Liana
4 Hummingbird
5 Macaw
6 Squirrel monkey
7 Three-toed sloth
8 Termite
9 Mouse
10 Herbivorous insects
11 Bat
12 Harpy eagle
13 Insectivorous bird
14 Basilisk lizard
15 Poison arrow frog
16 Ants
17 Ocelot
18 Dead animal
19 Blunt-headed tree snake
20 King vulture

Energy flow

Primary producer/primary consumer
Primary/secondary consumer
Secondary/tertiary consumer
Dead material/consumer

dioxide and water. The process by which this happens inside cells is called respiration, and it is the way all organisms, including plants, obtain energy to build and repair their own tissues, to reproduce, and to move about. The process of respiration is the reverse of photosynthesis.

Herbivores obtain energy by respiration. The sugar they need for respiration comes from the plants they eat. They do not gain all the sugar produced by photosynthesis because about 90 percent of it is used by the plants themselves in their own respiration.

Carnivores obtain the sugar they need for respiration from the animals they eat. Herbivores use about 90 percent of the sugars they eat to supply energy for their own bodies, so only about 10 percent remains for the carnivores. Top carnivores, which feed on other carnivores, also obtain only 10 percent of the sugars eaten by their prey.

Plants are known as "producers" because they are able to synthesize sugars from simple ingredients through photosynthesis. All animals are "consumers" because they cannot manufacture food for themselves in the way plants can, and they must obtain their sugars in ready-made form from plants or other animals.

Because such a large proportion of the energy originally produced is used in respiration at each feeding level, far fewer carnivores than herbivores can be supported by the system, and very few top carnivores.

Scavengers feed on the waste products and dead tissues from plants and animals. Fungi and bacteria then feed on what remains. They decompose large organic molecules, releasing smaller, simpler molecules that eventually dissolve and are absorbed into plant roots, completing the cycle. By that stage respiration

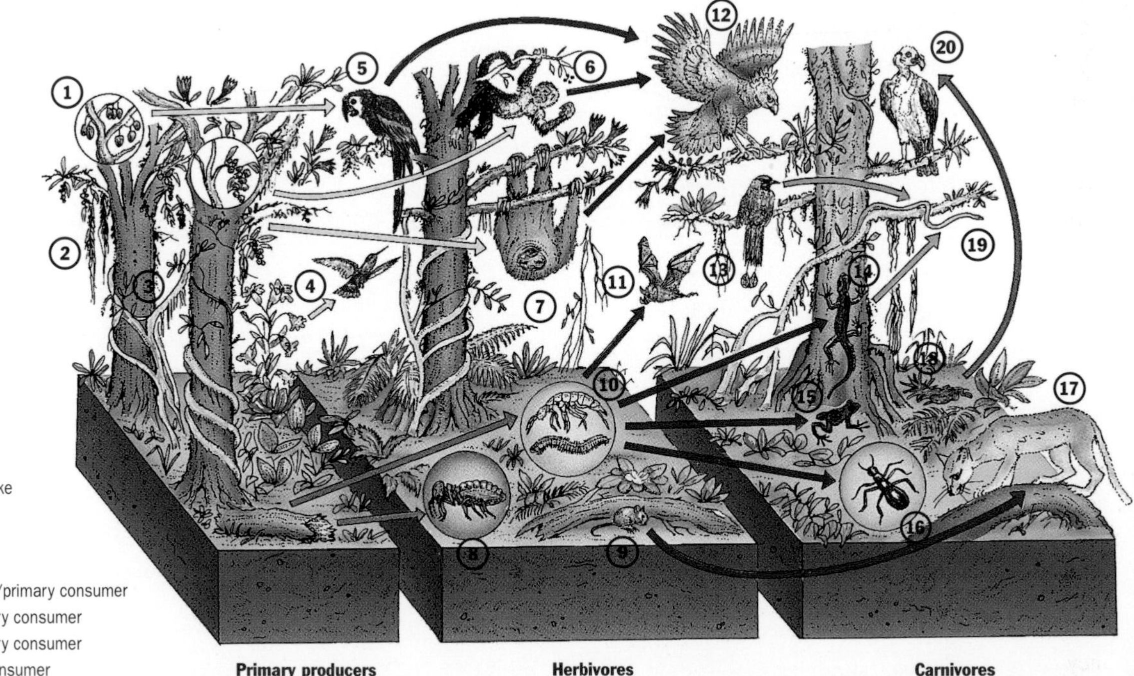

has oxidized all the sugars produced by photosynthesis.

FOREST COMMUNITIES

Producers, herbivores, and carnivores are linked to each other and to the physical and chemical conditions in which they all live. Together they form a community, or ecosystem. Tropical forest ecosystems work in the same way as ecosystems elsewhere, but they are complicated because they contain so many species.

In fact a tropical forest consists of many interconnected ecosystems. A single tree, for example, has beetles feeding in and beneath its bark. Insect-eating birds search for those beetles and their young (larvae). The birds build their nests on branches of the tree. They must be careful because there is also a snake in the tree, and it feeds on eggs and young birds. The birds do not have all the insects for themselves, either, because there are lizards that also eat them. The tree produces flowers containing nectar that is eaten by other insects or in some cases by hummingbirds. The leaves of the tree are food

THE BARRED LEAF FROG *(Phyllomedusa tomopterna)* lives above ground, climbing in trees. Suction pads on the tips of its fingers and toes ensure it never loses its grip, and its large eyes give it excellent vision for locating its insect prey. It lives in tropical South America.

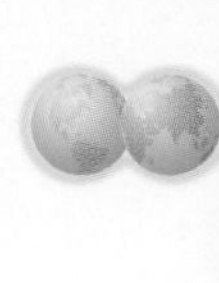

for a variety of animals, including leaf ants, monkeys, and sloths. Birds and monkeys also take the fruit.

Leaves that hang over water are used by leaf frogs, such as the barred leaf frog (*Phyllomedusa tomopterna*) of the South American lowland and cloud forests, to lay their eggs on. They fold the leaves into a purse to hold the eggs, and the female regularly sprays them with water to keep them moist. When the eggs hatch, the tadpoles drop into the water below.

Where a branch joins the main trunk, there may be a small depression—a hollow that fills with water. This tiny pool of water is home to single-celled plants and microscopic animals. The pool and its inhabitants may comprise a small ecosystem within the larger one of the whole tree.

The Third Dimension

Tree and leaf frogs, tree snakes, lizards, monkeys, and many other animals spend most or all of their lives in the trees. In all forests, but especially in tropical forests, much of the activity occurs above ground. Forests are three-dimensional environments.

The life of the forest above the ground is also arranged in layers. Many animals move about in search of food but rarely leave their own layer. Above the tops, or crowns, of the trees there are insects that have been pushed upward by air currents. Insect-eating birds and bats fly above the trees to hunt these insects. The crowns of the trees form a thick canopy, or forest cover. Birds and mammals living in the canopy feed on leaves, fruit, nectar, and insects.

In Asia mammals living in the canopy include gibbons (family Hylobatidae) and birds such as barbets (family Capitonidae), hornbills (Bucerotidae), and pigeons (Columbidae). At the level below them there are squirrels (family Sciuridae), monkeys (Cercopithecidae), woodpeckers (Picidae), bulbuls (Pycnonotidae), and trogons (Trogonidae). Other squirrel species, civets and genets (family Viverridae), thrushes

MACAWS ARE BIRDS OF THE SOUTH AMERICAN tropical forests; seen here are red and green *(Ara chloroptera)* and red and yellow *(A. macao)* macaws. These species nest in holes on cliff faces but feed in the forest canopy on fruit and seeds. Red and yellow (or scarlet) macaws are popular cage birds. Hunting has severely reduced their numbers in some areas.

FOREST LAYERS IN AN AFRICAN TROPICAL RAIN FOREST. Emergents (trees that rise above the forest) tower above the dense main canopy and are fully exposed to the wind. The crowns of trees forming the canopy are close enough together to support the trees. Plants of the understory (the underlying layer of vegetation) and of the herb layer grow in permanent shade.

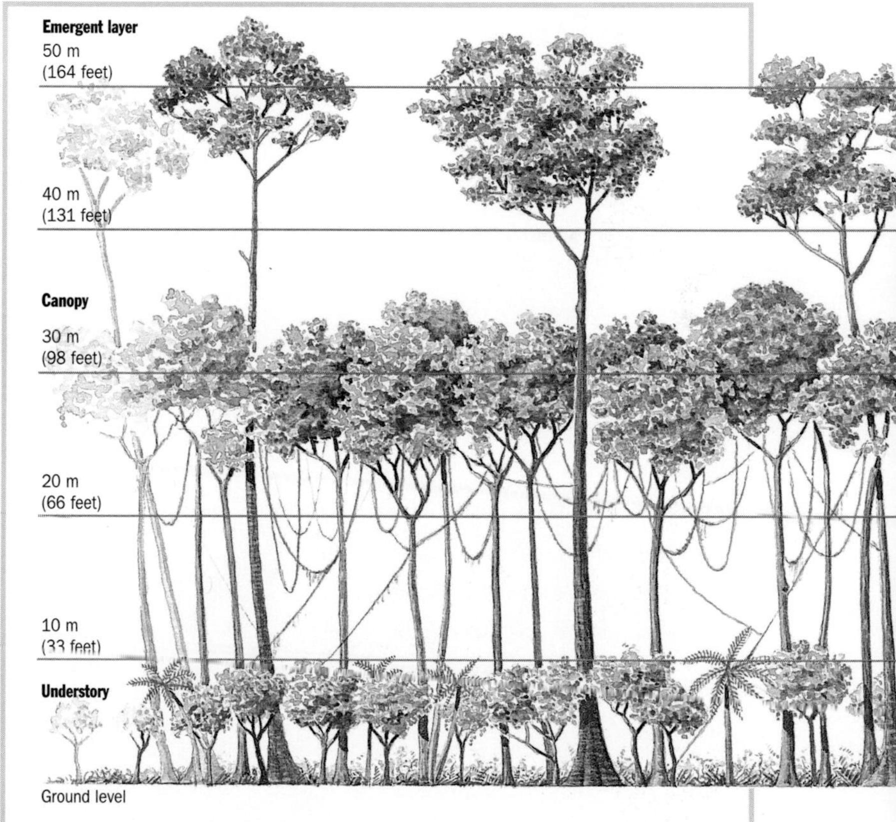

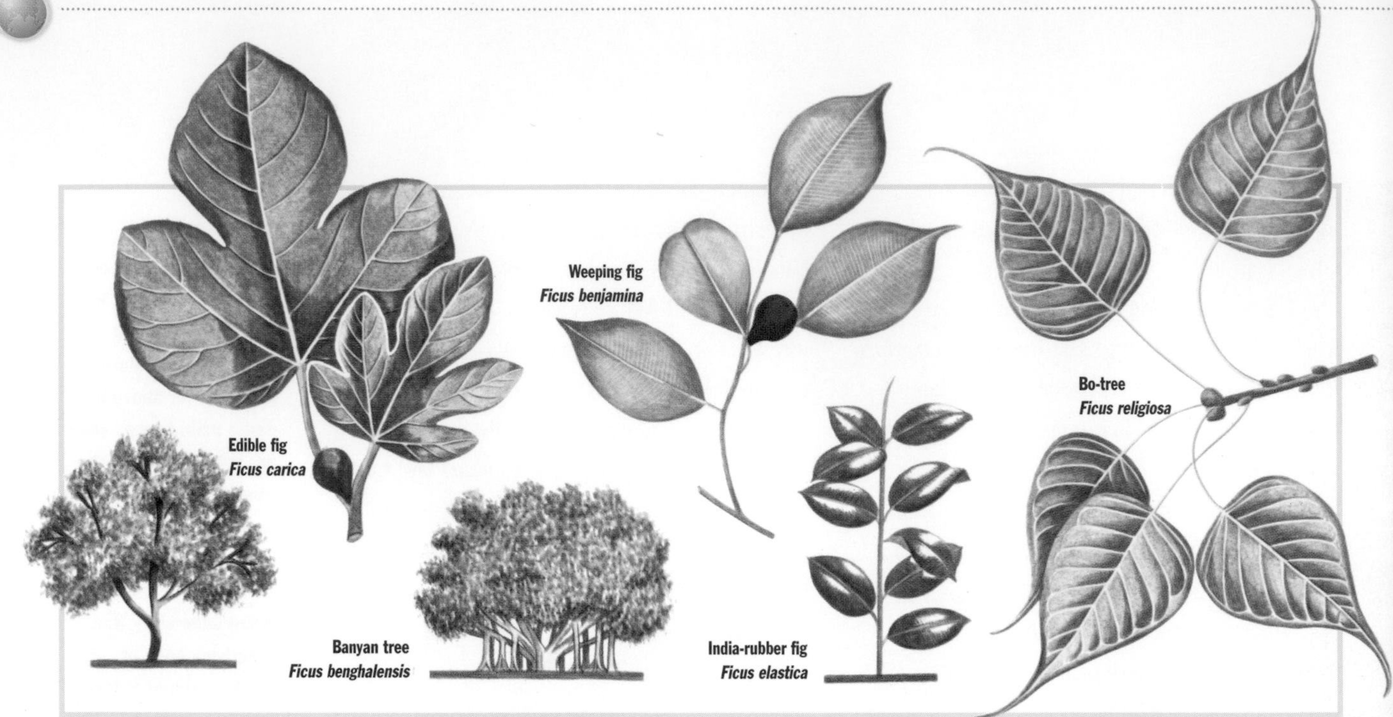

FIG TREES ***(above)*** **grow mainly in the tropics. There are more than 2,000 species. The edible fig is from southwest Asia, the weeping fig from Southeast Asia, and the bo-tree is from India. The India-rubber fig comes from India and Southeast Asia. The banyan tree produces roots that descend to form an open structure up to 65 feet (20 m) across.**

(Muscicapidae), babblers (subfamily Timaliinae), pittas (Pittidae), and pheasants (Phasianidae) are among the species that feed in the lower parts of the trees and on the ground.

As they move horizontally through the tropical forest, birds and mammals are quite systematic in their search for food. Many of the birds move in flocks, and monkeys and gibbons move around in troops. Species that eat fruit will pick some fruits in preference to others, and many of them will examine fruits carefully before they eat them, choosing only those that are absolutely ripe.

Troops of siamangs (*Hylobates syndactylus*), a species of gibbon, will strip trees of all their fruit whether or not it is ripe. The lar, or common gibbon (*H. lar*), lives in the same forests, but eats only the ripest fruit. With both species a troop usually consists of about four individuals. Leaf-eaters have more choice of food, but they often prefer young, tender leaves and leaves only from particular plants.

FOREST TREES

Animals live and feed at different levels because the trees themselves are at different heights. The trees form layers, or storys, although these are not always easy to see amid the confusion of a living forest.

Often there are three layers of trees. The topmost story comprises the tallest trees, called emergents because they stand above the main forest canopy, together with the climbing plants that reach their crowns and the smaller plants growing on them. The crowns of the emergents are more than 80 feet (25 m) above ground level; in places they may reach twice that height.

The middle tree layer comprises trees and climbers between 33 and 80 feet (10 and 25 m) tall. This is the layer in which the crowns of the trees touch one another to form a complete canopy. Some of the trees in this layer belong to the same species as the emergents.

A lower tree layer, or understory, consists of trees and climbers 16 to 33 feet (5 to 10 m) tall. These include saplings of the species forming the middle layer that will grow to their full height as soon as a large tree falls, producing a gap in the canopy through which light can penetrate. There are also smaller trees that are able to grow in shade.

Below the main tree layers there is a shrub layer. It contains tree seedlings, shrubs, and small trees from 3 to 16 feet (1 to 5 m) tall. Beneath them there is a herb layer, comprising small, nonwoody plants and young tree seedlings. Because the ground is shaded, plants of the herb layer rarely cover more than about 10 percent of the surface.

Standing Tall

Emergent trees stand with their crowns high above the canopy. This allows them uninterrupted exposure to sunlight. In the canopy itself the tops of the crowns are well lit, but leaves lower down are shaded. Clearly, the emergents have an advantage—but they must pay for it. They are also fully exposed to the wind—and 80 feet (25 m) or more above the ground the wind can be fierce. The trees must be strong enough to withstand it.

Tree roots can extend to about 10 feet (3 m) below the ground surface, although in a tropical forest few of the "feeding roots," through

BUTTRESS ROOTS *(left)* grow from trunks up to 10 feet (3 m) above ground level. They help support tall emergent trees. Smaller trees have similar roots that emerge much lower down. The feeding roots of these trees lie just beneath the surface, absorbing nutrients released by the rapid decomposition of dead plants.

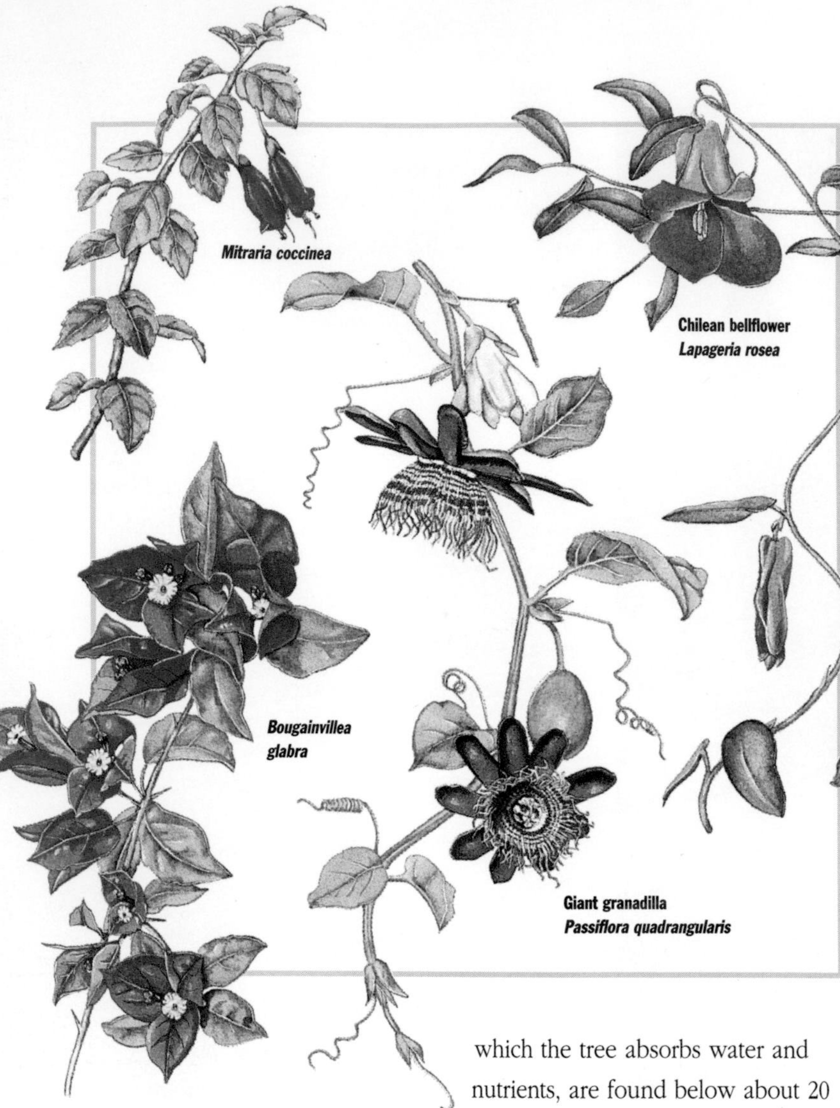

SOUTH AMERICAN CLIMBERS. Many forest climbers have brightly colored flowers to attract pollinators. Some, such as the giant granadilla, produce edible fruit. Bougainvilleas are widely cultivated for the beautiful bracts (a type of leaf)—usually red or purple—that surround the flowers.

which the tree absorbs water and nutrients, are found below about 20 inches (50 cm). Roots do not provide very secure anchorage for emergent trees that are being blown about by strong winds; many do not have roots reaching deep below ground. Instead, their roots spread horizontally and many of them merge into each other. Often these roots emerge from the trunk of the tree up to 10 feet (3 m) above ground level and form huge buttresses, or supports.

Other species grow roots that emerge from the trunk at about the same height as buttress roots, but then grow away from the trunk before turning to grow downward. These roots form stilts. Like buttresses, they support the tree, and both types of root reach only a few inches into the ground.

Life is easier for trees of the canopy layer. They grow so close together that their crowns touch. The wind blows over them, but the trees are sheltered, and to some extent they can lean against each other.

LOOKING FOR SUPPORT

Some trees never bother to grow a trunk of their own. Instead, they use the trunk of another species. Climbers use trees for support, of course, but the stranglers go much further. They take trees over completely. There are many unrelated species of stranglers, but fig trees (*Ficus* species) are the best known.

The life of a strangling fig begins when a bird drops a seed onto the branch of a large tree, which comes to rest in a hollow that contains a little water. The seed germinates (sprouts), and the fig grows as an epiphyte (see page 25): it obtains the nutrients it needs from the water on the bark of the tree, but it is not a parasite (an organism that lives off another organism).

Then the fig produces roots. These grow down the sides of the trunk of the tree all the way to the ground, where they produce feeding roots. The fig produces more and more roots, all of them clinging closely to the trunk of the tree, and they supply the fig plant with enough water and nutrients for it to grow to a large size, with branches and leaves of its own. Eventually, the

crown of the fig tree may grow larger than the crown of the tree on which it is growing.

Meanwhile, the fig roots grow thicker and more numerous until they envelop the trunk. The roots press hard against each other and they merge or *anastomose*. The bark disappears where the roots are in contact so they all grow into each other. Fig roots then form a case surrounding the trunk of the original tree, which often dies. In this way a forest tree of another species is replaced by a fig tree.

Climbers

Stranglers grow from the top down. By germinating high in the forest canopy, their seedlings have an immediate advantage—they are exposed to sunlight. Life is much more difficult for plants growing in the deep shade

BROMELIADS growing on the rough bark of a tree in the South American rain forest. Bromeliads are epiphytes and store water for their own use. If too many of them grow on the same branch, their combined weight may break it.

beneath the canopy, particularly those forest plants that cannot grow high enough to reach the light. There is an alternative, however, and the plants making use of it are highly visible. They are the lianes—vines and other climbing plants that often hang from trees like thick ropes.

Like stranglers, climbers have found an economical way to reach the sunlight in the forest canopy. Unlike stranglers, they grow from seeds that germinate in the ground, so they begin life in openings in the forest or near the edge of forests, where sunlight reaches the surface. This is why they are common beside rivers, roads, and railroads, but uncommon deep inside the forest, except where logging has created openings.

The young climber succeeds if it can attach itself to the crown of a tree seedling. Then, as the young tree grows, the climber grows with it. The climber is not a parasite—it does not take nutrients from the tree but uses it only for support. By the time the tree attains its full size, its companion the climber will also be big, often with a thick, woody stem and a crown that can sometimes be as big as that of the tree itself. Climbers of this type are attached to the crown of the tree, not its trunk, so they hang free. Their stems can measure up to 5 inches (13 cm) in diameter.

There are many species of woody climbers. Most species of *Gnetum* are climbers. Thick rings, or hoops, grow at intervals along the stem, making *Gnetum* climbers easily recognizable. Rattans are another species that it is easy to recognize, because their stems produce rings of long, sharp spines. Rattans are palms, and, despite their fierce spines, people use them to make a wide variety of articles including ropes, baskets, furniture, and mats. They also yield a resin that is used in lacquers and also has medicinal properties. Cane furniture sold in America and Europe is usually made from rattan and bamboo.

Other climbers work differently. They grow up the trunk of the tree, clinging to it. Ivy can be seen growing this way in temperate as well as in

THE BIGGEST FLOWER IN THE WORLD *(above)*, measuring more than 3 feet (1 m) across, grows on the floor of the tropical forests of Southeast Asia and smells of rotting meat. It belongs to *Rafflesia arnoldii* and is a parasite that produces neither stem nor leaves.

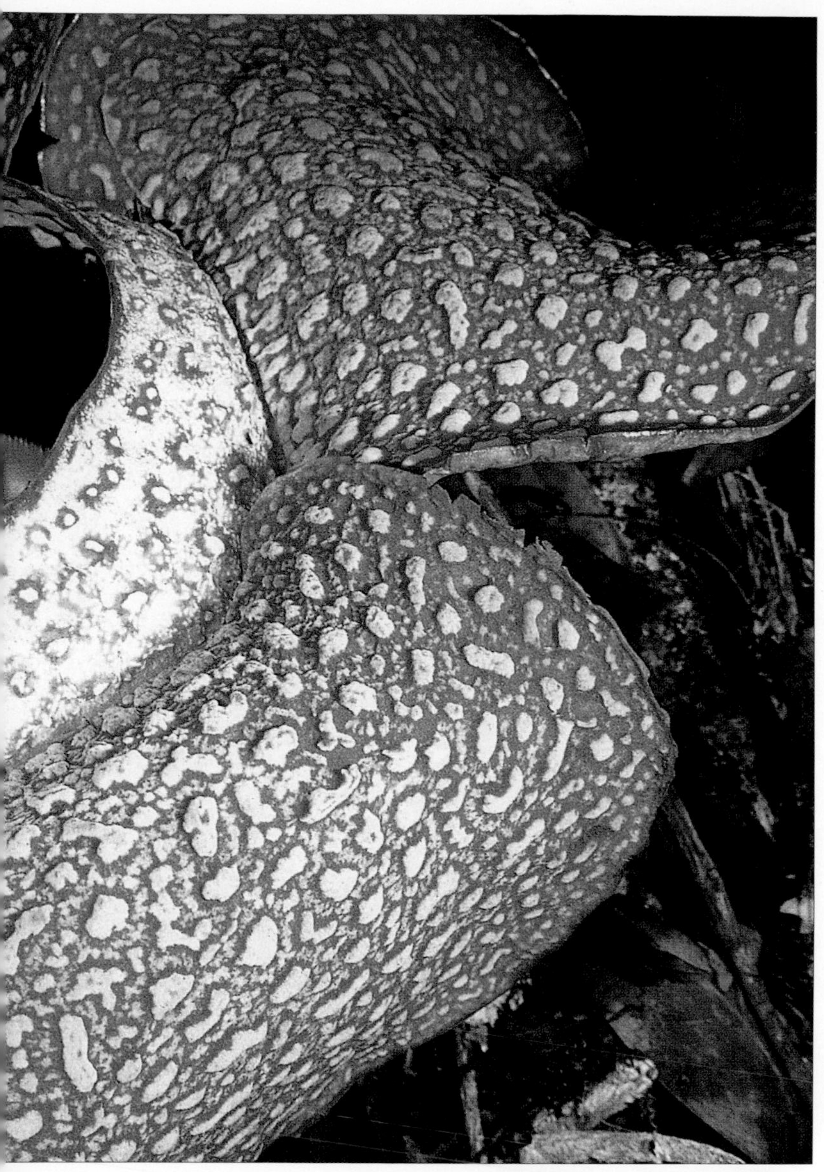

Epiphytes and Parasites

Many tropical trees produce flowers directly on their bark. This is called cauliflory. Flowers or leaves growing on the bark of a tree may not belong to that tree, however. They may be part of an entirely different plant. In temperate forests many trees have lichens and mosses growing on their bark, and ferns growing along their branches.

Plants that grow on other plants are called epiphytes, and there are many more of them in tropical forests than there are anywhere else. Some, known as epiphylls, grow on the surface of leaves. They include ferns, mosses, liverworts, lichens, and algae related to those found in temperate forests, but there are also many flowering plants. Orchids and species of *Vaccinium*, relatives of the blueberry and cranberry, grow as epiphytes high in the canopy of Asian forests. There are also orchids in South American forests, as well as bromeliads (family Bromeliaceae) and even some cacti.

The cacti provide a clue to the problem all epiphytes face. They have no contact with the ground, and, despite the heavy rainfall, the bark

PITCHER PLANTS, such as *Nepenthes macfarlanei (opposite)* of the family Nepenthaceae, have leaves in the shape of pitchers; insects that fall into them cannot escape. Some pitchers hold nearly 2 quarts (2.2 liters) of digestive fluid, enough to drown a rat.

tropical regions; most members of the ivy genus (*Hedera*) are tropical. The leaves of one trunk-climber, *Freycinetia reineckei*, which grows in Samoa, are used to make skirts, and its fibers are woven into cloth.

Smaller, nonwoody climbers also climb on trunks, but sometimes lose their hold. Then they hang free, like ropes. When these reach the ground, they take root and then seek another tree to climb.

or leaves on which they grow are often dry, especially if an opening suddenly appears in the canopy and they are exposed to direct sunshine. Epiphytes must be tolerant of drought that can occur suddenly and without warning. Some store water and resist drying, others allow themselves to wilt, but prevent their cells from losing water, so they revive quickly when they are wetted.

Some epiphytes live partly as parasites (called hemiparasites), producing roots that penetrate the host plant and absorb water and nutrients from it, but also producing sugars by photosynthesis. Members of the mistletoe family (Loranthaceae) are hemiparasites, and most of them occur in the tropics.

The most unusual parasite produces the world's biggest flower and possibly its most evil-smelling one. *Rafflesia arnoldii* lives as a mass of minute threads inside the roots of lianes belonging to the genus *Tetrastigma*. It produces no stem or leaves, only a huge flower that grows on the ground and smells of rotting meat. The smell attracts the flies that pollinate the plant.

Carnivorous Plants

Plant nutrients are scarce in the tropical forest environment. The soil is poor, and the extensive feeding roots of the trees quickly absorb nutrients as they are released through the decay of organic (carbon-containing) material. Among the smaller plants some have evolved to exploit a different source of nutrients: they are carnivorous.

Pitcher plants are the best known and the most common of the carnivorous plants. There are 17 species in the family Sarraceniaceae, found in North and South America, and about 70 in the Nepenthaceae, occurring from Madagascar to southern and Southeast Asia and Australia. The American species grow in bogs and similar places where nutrients are limited. Many

BIGGEST OF ALL THE CATS, the tiger is possibly the most famous animal of southern Asia. It lives in forests of all types, including monsoon forest, although hunting and alteration of its habitat have greatly reduced its numbers.

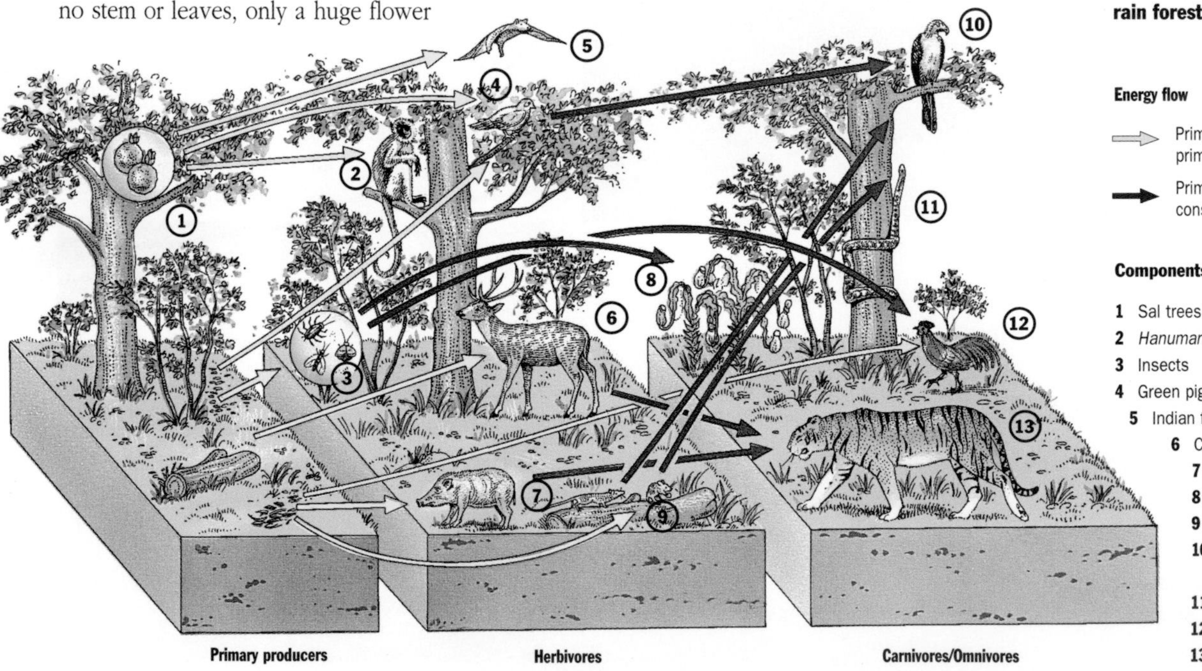

THE ECOSYSTEM OF A MONSOON FOREST **comprises species tolerant of the strongly seasonal climate and often poor soil that makes it more open than rain forest.**

Nepenthaceae species are epiphytes, but most are woody climbers.

Pitchers of Sarraceniaceae are modified leaves that grow directly from an underground stem called a rhizome. Some species of pitcher emit a strong smell to attract insects; others release nectar or use bright colors. Once an insect alights it is likely to slip down into the pitcher, over hairs that project downward and prevent it from climbing out.

In the Nepenthaceae the pitchers develop from the thick vein, called the midrib, that runs along the center of every leaf. The ends of the midribs grow into pitchers with lids. The lid opens when the pitcher is mature. "Honey glands" at the mouth of the pitcher release a sweet-tasting substance that is attractive to insects. Once an insect enters, it slides down the very slippery surface and is trapped.

Pitchers contain water in which the prey drown and digestive juices that liquefy them. The

A TIGER HUNTS by stalking its prey. Its body stripes help it blend into the background. When it is about 60 feet (18 m) away, it breaks cover, rushing toward its victim from the side or behind, and lashing out with its paws. This panics the prey long enough for the tiger to bring it down with its claws. The prey is killed with a bite to the neck or throat.

nutrients then pass into the plant. Some species grow pitchers about 2 inches (5 cm) long, others are even bigger, and in Borneo there are *Nepenthes* plants with pitchers that hold nearly 2 quarts (2.2 liters) of water and can digest animals the size of a small rodent.

MONSOONS AND THE FOREST

In winter air pressure is high over most of the continent of Asia. Air is subsiding and flowing outward as very dry winds. These northerly and northeasterly winds blow across the Indian subcontinent and China, bringing extremely dry weather. This is known as the winter, or dry, monsoon.

In summer the situation is different. The land warms, producing low pressure as air is heated by contact with the ground, expands, and rises. Low pressure draws in air as southwesterly winds blowing across the Indian Ocean. These are moist because they have crossed the ocean, and they bring heavy rain. This has little effect north of the Himalayas because air flowing northward loses its moisture as it is forced to rise. In southern Asia it brings the wet, or summer, monsoon.

Africa, Australia, and America also experience monsoon seasons, but they are much

THE RED PANDA lives in the bamboo forests of southern China and the Himalayan foothills, feeding on a variety of fruits, nuts, roots, and probably meat, as well as bamboo shoots. It is not closely related to the giant panda.

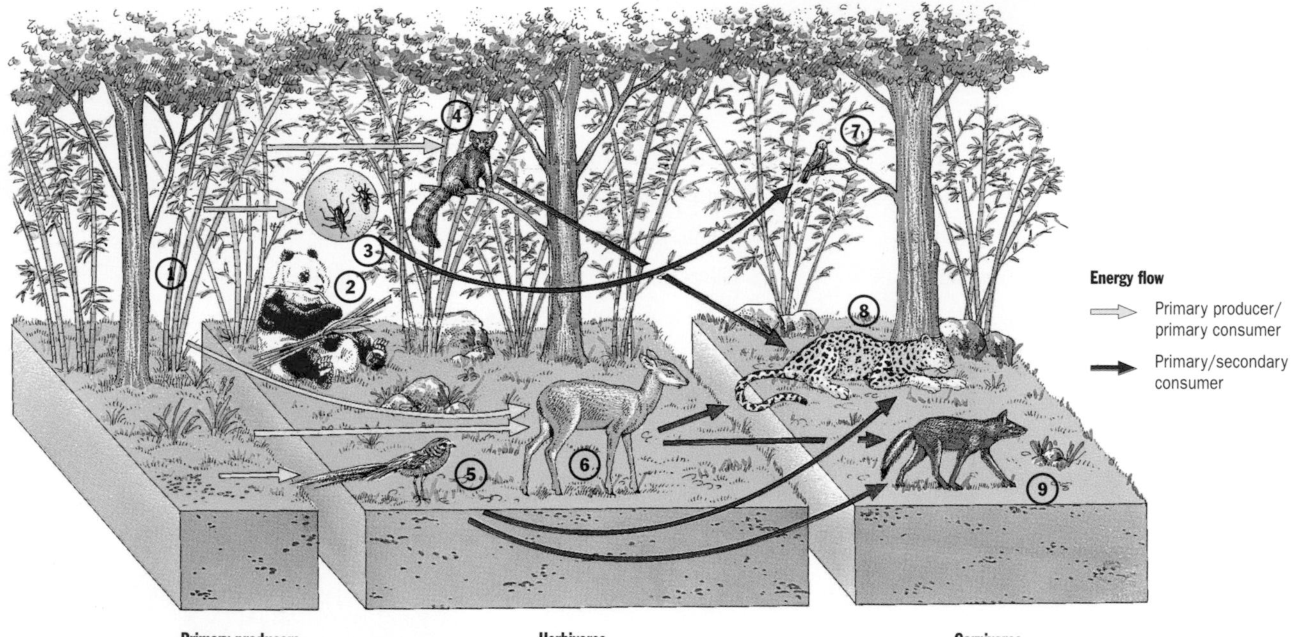

Components of the ecosystem

1 Bamboo
2 Giant panda
3 Herbivorous insects
4 Red panda
5 Golden pheasant
6 Musk deer
7 Red-breasted fly-catcher
8 Leopard
9 Golden jackal

A BAMBOO FOREST ECOSYSTEM. Life in the bamboo forest relies heavily on the bamboo. When it dies, food shortages affect all the animals in the ecosystem of the bamboo forest, not simply the giant panda, which feeds mainly on bamboo shoots and leaves.

less marked than those of Asia, where the effect is striking. Bombay, for example, receives an average 4 inches (104 mm) of rain between October and May and 67 inches (1,707 mm) between June and September.

Life in the Monsoon Forest

In the monsoon forest trees adapt to the seasonal climate by shedding their leaves in the dry season. Plants time their flowering and seed production to coincide with the arrival of the rains. Conditions vary from place to place, however. What matters is the availability of water. Some soils retain moisture better than others, and plants growing near rivers and lakes have access to water throughout the year. Monsoon forest forms a complex patchwork of species, the composition depending on the moisture below ground.

In Africa the seasonal forest is very open, with grasses growing between the trees. Asian monsoon forest is more closed, but sufficiently open for the ground to be dappled with sunshine. In Thailand the most common trees are *Dipterocarpus tuberculatus* and *D. obtusifolius*—a tree often found near rivers; its local name is *neram*, which means "rivers." These are both important timber trees, and *Dipterocarpus* species are widespread in Asian rain forests as well as monsoon forests.

Two other important species—sal and teak—grow in the monsoon forests of India and Myanmar (Burma). Pitcher plants (*Nepenthes*) grow in places that are permanently wet.

THE BAMBOO FOREST

Bamboos are grasses, belonging to the subfamily Bambusoideae of the grass family Gramineae. There are about 100 genera and hundreds of species. Most species grow well in a wet but cool tropical climate at elevations above 6,000 feet (1,830 m). Trees are more widely spaced at these heights, and bamboos replace them. Bamboos flourish on high ground in southern

China and in the foothills of the Himalayas. In places they can grow to a height of 130 feet (40 m), and they always form dense thickets. Wherever they occur, they are abundant.

Bamboo-Eaters

Most species of bamboo have commercial uses, and the shoots and leaves of many are edible. Forests of bamboo therefore provide food for many animals. The red panda (*Ailurus fulgens*), a relative of the raccoon, eats bamboo as part of its diet, but the most famous bamboo-eater is the giant panda (*Ailuropoda melanoleuca*), a member of the bear family (Ursidae). It is sometimes called the "bamboo bear." Giant pandas live in the bamboo forests between 8,500 feet and 11,500 feet (2,600 m and 3,500 m) and spend up to 12 hours every day feeding.

Giant pandas hold bamboo stalks in their paws, manipulating them skillfully. Humans manipulate objects by moving their thumbs against their fingers—human thumbs are "opposable." At first glance the giant panda appears to have an opposable thumb too, but a close look at its paws reveals that the panda has six digits instead of the usual five, and its thumb is not really a thumb at all. It is an enlargement of what in other animals is a small wrist bone called the radial sesmoid. The wrist muscles are also modified to allow the bone to be used like a thumb. Other bears (and the red panda) have a slightly enlarged radial sesmoid, but only in the giant panda is it the size of a thumb.

Flowering Bamboos

Some bamboos flower every year like other plants, but many of them flower only once in their lives. After flowering and producing seeds, the plants die, to be replaced by new plants growing from the seeds.

Plants that flower only once are said to be hapaxanthic. The point at which hapaxanthic bamboos flower varies according to species. It can be from every ten years to every 150 years. Species in the genus *Bambusa*, for example, flower every 150 years.

The curious thing about their flowering is that it is synchronized. When it is time for a bamboo species to flower, every plant belonging to that species flowers at the same time, no matter where in the world it is. Then all the plants die together.

Flowering is a rare event, and it drastically alters the bamboo forest. Some years ago *Sinarundinaria nitida* flowered and died after about 100 years. It is one of the species on which giant pandas depend, but pandas have lived with the hapaxanthic bamboos for a very long time. They know how to find other food.

Great hornbill
Buceros bicornis

CONVERGENT EVOLUTION

Thousands of miles of ocean separate America, Africa, and Asia. Tropical forests grow in all three regions, but the forest plants and animals in one are completely isolated from those in the others. Despite this, some of the species bear a

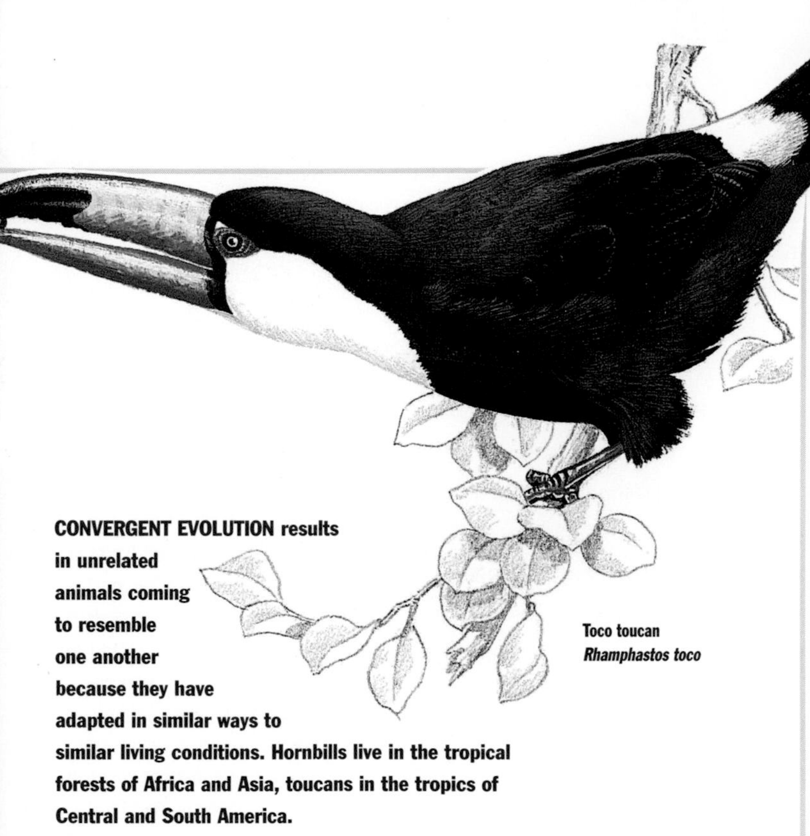

Toco toucan
Rhamphastos toco

CONVERGENT EVOLUTION results in unrelated animals coming to resemble one another because they have adapted in similar ways to similar living conditions. Hornbills live in the tropical forests of Africa and Asia, toucans in the tropics of Central and South America.

remarkable resemblance to each other, even though they are not closely related. Asian and African monkeys, for example, have been separated from American monkeys for about 50 million years, and there are now several important differences between them. Yet they live and behave in similar ways and look very alike. Pigs that live in the forests of Africa and Asia look much like the peccaries that live in American forests, although pigs and peccaries are not close relatives.

These apparent coincidences arise because there are limits to the number of ways a species can adapt its body and lifestyle to the environment in which it lives. Ants and termites are plentiful in tropical regions, for example, so it is not surprising that various mammal species feed on them. To help them do so, they have acquired strong claws on their front feet for tearing into anthills and termite mounds, and long snouts and tongues for taking up small insects. At the same time their teeth have become very small or have disappeared. This general description applies to a number of unrelated animals. The long-beaked echidna (*Zaglossus bruijni*) is a monotreme (egg-laying mammal) that lives in New Guinea. The numbat (*Myrmecobius fasciatus*) is a marsupial (pouched mammal) from Australia. The aardvark (*Orycteropus afer*)—a mammal not closely related to any other—lives in Africa. Pangolins—seven species of mammals comprising the family Manidae—are found in Africa and Asia. Anteaters—four species comprising the family Myrmecophagidae—occur in Central and South America.

When unrelated plants or animals evolve to resemble each other because they have adapted in similar ways to similar situations, the process is called convergent evolution, or convergence. There are many examples, and in the past they have misled people into assuming that animals sharing particular features were necessarily related. Elephants and rhinoceroses, for example, were once grouped together as "pachyderms" because of their thick skins, but the two groups are not closely related.

BIRDS OF THE FOREST

Many species of hornbills and toucans live in tropical forests. Hornbills fly through the forest in large flocks. Toucan flocks are smaller and less compact. Hornbills and toucans are large

birds that feed mainly on fruit and seeds, but also on insects and other small animals, and they nest in holes, usually in trees. They have a huge bill, often with serrations like small saw-teeth near the tip. In some species this is brightly colored. Some hornbills also have brightly colored feathers or bare skin on the face and throat. Many hornbills, but not toucans, have a structure called a casque on top of the bill. This is large in some species and probably helps birds identify each other.

The bill looks unwieldy, but the birds use it very cleverly. Fruits are seized with the tip of the bill, then tossed back into the gullet with a flick of the head. The serrations are used to cut up larger food items.

In most hornbill species, once a female has laid her eggs, she seals the entrance to the nest with mud and her own droppings—in some species she will be helped by the male—leaving only a narrow slit. She remains there until some time after the chicks have hatched. While she is sealed inside the nest, she loses all her feathers, then grows new ones. The male feeds her through this opening, and she throws out uneaten food and droppings. When the chicks are about half-grown, the female breaks out of the nest, and the chicks seal it again behind her. She then joins the male in providing food for them until they are old enough to fly, when they break free.

Although they also nest in holes, toucans do not seal them. Instead, both parents share the task of keeping the eggs warm (incubating them) and then feeding the chicks.

Because they share so many features of physical appearance as well as feeding and nesting habits, it seems natural to assume hornbills and toucans are closely related. In fact, they are quite unrelated. Hornbills comprise 45 species in the family Bucerotidae and belong to the order Coraciiformes. The 38 species of toucans comprise the family Rhamphastidae of the order Piciformes. Both groups live in the same way, and their similarities are the result. They have arisen through convergent evolution.

Quetzals, Hoatzins, and Parrots

Hornbills and toucans are colorful, but there are other birds of the tropical forests to outshine them. One of these, the resplendent quetzal (*Pharomachrus mocinno*), lives in the cloud forests of Central America. It has a metallic green back and head and a bright red breast, belly, and underside of its tail. The male also has brilliant green tail feathers that are twice the length of its body; he displays them to attract a mate by flying high above the forest canopy. The tail is shed at the end of each breeding season, and new feathers are produced in time for the next.

Quetzal tail feathers were used ceremonially by Aztec (Mexican Indian) people in the 15th and 16th centuries; the bird was sacred and associated with the serpent god Quetzalcoatl. The quetzal is now the national bird of Guatemala, and the unit of currency. Some people believe it is the most beautiful bird in the world.

Farther south the hoatzin (*Opisthocomus hoazin*) lives in the lowland rain forests of northern South America. Related to the cuckoos (order Cuculiformes), the hoatzin is about 24 inches (60 cm) long and attractively colored, although it is not a spectacular bird like the quetzal. It is famed more for its behavior.

COLORFUL PLUMAGE allows birds of the tropical forests to recognize members of their own species amid the profusion of greenery and brilliant flowers. As a result, these forests are home to some of the most spectacular birds in the world as well as some of the most unusual. Young hoatzin climb with the help of claws on their wings. The resplendent quetzal was once associated with a god and is now the national bird of Guatemala.

Magnificent riflebird
Ptiloris magnificus
Resplendent quetzal
Pharomachrus mocinno
Hyacinthine macaw
Anodorhynchus hyacinthinus
Hoatzin
Opisthocomus hoazin
Superb bird of paradise
Lophorina superba
Victoria crowned pigeon
Goura victoria

Hoatzins are weak fliers. They prefer to glide from tree to tree, climbing from branch to branch to gain height. They are also very strictly vegetarian, feeding only on leaves. Their chicks hatch high in the forest, and the parents bring leaves to feed them. As the parents approach, the chicks leave the nest and scramble through the tree, eager to seize the approaching meal. To help them climb, they have small claws on the leading edges of their wings.

False vampire bat
Vampyrum spectrum

If threatened, a hoatzin chick simply drops out of the tree into the water below. Then it swims to the foot of its tree and climbs all the way back up to the nest.

Parrots are the most famous birds of tropical forests. There are more than 320 species of them, and they are found throughout the tropics and in Australia. Most are brightly colored.

Their distinctive bill is a versatile tool, more mobile than the bill of most birds because the upper part is attached to the skull by a kind of hinge. With its bill a parrot can gently preen its feathers or crack very hard nutshells. It can also climb, using its bill like a third claw. Its feet are also unusual in that its two outer toes point backward and its two inner toes point forward—this condition is called zygodactyly. It allows a parrot to grip its perch very tightly, and also to use its claw to manipulate objects, as if it were a hand.

Courtship Displays

Males of many species of birds seek to attract mates by congregating in a particular area, called a lek, and then competing for the most prominent position. Females visit the lek and choose the male they find most attractive. This is usually the male that performs the best dance or has the best plumage. Competition among males

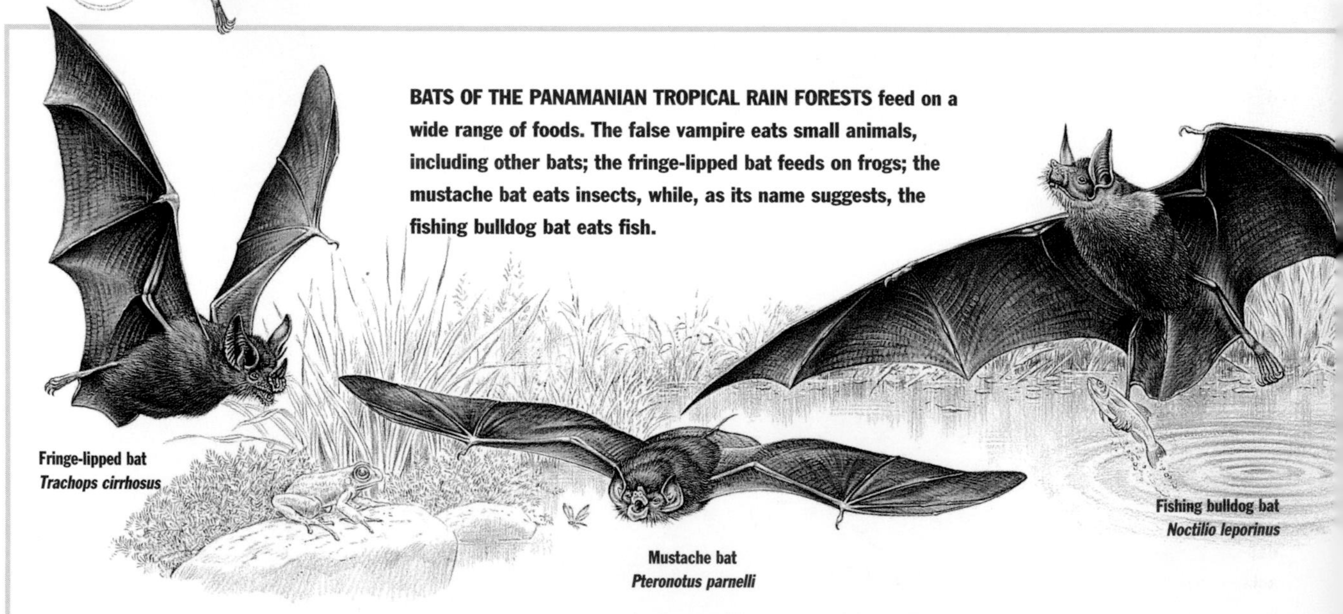

BATS OF THE PANAMANIAN TROPICAL RAIN FORESTS feed on a wide range of foods. The false vampire eats small animals, including other bats; the fringe-lipped bat feeds on frogs; the mustache bat eats insects, while, as its name suggests, the fishing bulldog bat eats fish.

and the preference of females for a particular feature or type of behavior has led to the evolution of extremes, such as the tail of a male peacock.

Courtship of this kind is common in the rain and montane forests of New Guinea and the nearby islands, where it has produced the 43 species of birds of paradise. Their leks may be on the ground or high in the trees, where males show off their gaudy plumage as they strut along branches, and in some cases hang upside down.

Groups of male superb birds of paradise (*Lophorina superba*) display right up in the forest canopy. Like most birds of paradise, once he has won a female and mated, the male leaves the female and goes off to seek other mates. The female is left to build the nest of twigs, incubate the eggs, and raise the young.

The magnificent riflebird (*Ptiloris magnificus*) is also a bird of paradise, and it, too, performs its courtship display on a branch high in the canopy. Its "dance" involves throwing back its head and waving it from side to side to expose the brilliant feathers on its throat and breast, at the same time holding out its wings, which have an unusual, rounded shape. As with the superb bird of paradise, the male will leave the female to build the nest and raise the family alone.

COLUCOS, OR FLYING LEMURS, live in southern Asia and some Pacific islands. They inhabit forests, gliding from tree to tree, but they cannot flap their wings to achieve true flight.

These are not the only birds to perform elaborate courtship rituals in the tropical forests of New Guinea and Australia. Male bowerbirds use sticks, leaves, and other plant material to construct a kind of stage in an open space on the forest floor. They then decorate their "bowers" with flowers, mosses, brightly colored berries, and a variety of other small objects. The male waits on or near his bower, and when a female passes, he tries to lure her inside. There are 18 species of bowerbirds. Each builds its own distinctive type of bower, and some steal ornaments from their neighbors. Scientists have traced particular items of ornament as they are taken from bower to bower, sometimes for a considerable distance.

There is even a pigeon that displays on the forest floor. More than 2 feet (60 cm) long, the Victoria crowned pigeon (*Goura victoria*) is probably the largest pigeon in the world. The male has a crest of feathers on his head and blue, white-tipped tail feathers. He displays by erecting his crest, spreading his tail, and performing a series of deep bows.

BIRDS ARE NOT THE ONLY FLIERS

So much of the food in a tropical forest is high above the ground that many animals live permanently in the trees. This presents them with the problem of moving from tree to tree without climbing down to the ground and back up again. Many have learned to glide from one tree to another. They lose height during the glide, but have only a short distance to climb back to their previous level—and jumping off a branch is a quick and effective way to escape from a predator.

Apart from birds, bats comprise the only group of vertebrate animals (animals with backbones and a skull) to have mastered true flight—flying by flapping their wings so they can

gain height and remain airborne for as long as they choose. Bats have very long arms and extremely long fingers. A layer of tough skin covers the "frame" formed from their outstretched arms and fingers and is attached to their shoulders, hind limbs, and tail. This skin makes up the wings of a bat.

There are two main groups of bats, the Megachiroptera and the Microchiroptera. Megachiroptera (fruit bats) feed on fruit. They are sometimes called flying foxes because they have long, rather foxlike faces. There are about 170 species of them, and they all live in the tropics. Microchiroptera are much smaller, and, unlike the fruit bats, they use sound to navigate and locate food. They have large, sensitive ears to receive sound, and curious fleshy structures on their faces. These act like megaphones, focusing the very high-pitched calls that the bats make into narrow beams. The bats are able to discern the direction and distance of objects as the sound is reflected back to them. This is called echolocation. There are more than 700 species of Microchiroptera. They occur throughout the world, but there are more species in the tropics than anywhere else.

Bats are the only mammals capable of true flight, but they are not the only ones to have wings made from skin stretched between their limbs and tail. The colugos or flying lemurs (two species in the genus *Cynocephalus*) have wings of this kind, but can use them only for gliding—although they can glide a long way. They are not true lemurs, and scientists are not sure whether they are related to bats, primates (the order that includes lemurs, monkeys, and apes), or whether they have no close mammal relatives. They live in Asia, are active only at night, and eat plants. In southern Asia there is also a squirrel—the red-and-white giant flying squirrel (*Petaurista alborufa*)—that glides in this way.

Flying Lizards, Snakes, and Frogs

There is no such thing as a dragon, but there is a lizard called the flying dragon (*Draco volans*) that lives in southern Asia. About 8 inches (20 cm) long, it can extend its ribs to the sides, stretching out a flap of skin that works like a parachute. The "dragon" can glide easily from one tree to the next. It feeds on insects.

Another lizard, the flying gecko (*Ptychozoon kuhli*) of Malaysia and Indonesia, can also extend its ribs. Its "parachute" is smaller than that of the flying dragon, but it also extends flaps of skin on either side of its tail and legs, and all its feet are webbed.

There is even a snake that can "fly." The paradise tree snake (*Chrysopelea paradisi*), also of southern Asia, glides by flattening its body and pulling in its belly. It can cover about 60

SLOTHS ARE THE SLOWEST of all mammals *(top left)*. They live in the tropical rain forests of Central and South America and feed on leaves. Their big, hooked claws allow them to hang upside down, but prevent them from walking well on the ground, where they can only drag themselves along. They do, however, swim well.

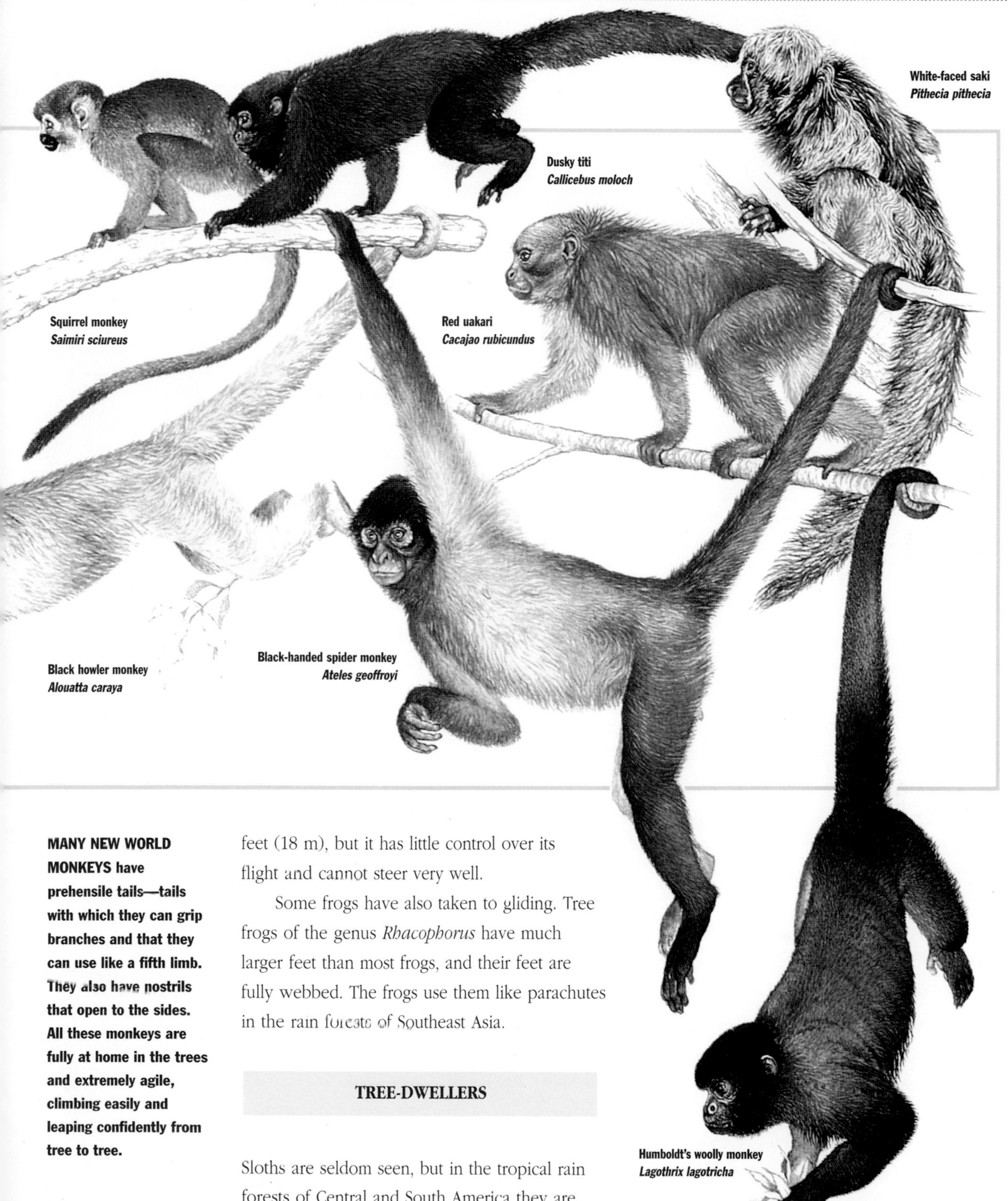

MANY NEW WORLD MONKEYS have prehensile tails—tails with which they can grip branches and that they can use like a fifth limb. They also have nostrils that open to the sides. All these monkeys are fully at home in the trees and extremely agile, climbing easily and leaping confidently from tree to tree.

feet (18 m), but it has little control over its flight and cannot steer very well.

Some frogs have also taken to gliding. Tree frogs of the genus *Rhacophorus* have much larger feet than most frogs, and their feet are fully webbed. The frogs use them like parachutes in the rain forests of Southeast Asia.

TREE-DWELLERS

Sloths are seldom seen, but in the tropical rain forests of Central and South America they are

fairly common. There are two genera of two-toed (*Choloepus*) and three-toed (*Bradypus*) sloths, with a total of five species. They are fully adapted to life in the trees, rarely visiting the ground. Depending on the species, their toes have two or three huge, hooked claws that allow them to hang upside down without discomfort. Three-toed sloths have fur that grows in the opposite direction from the fur of most mammals, so it points down. Each hair has a groove in which single-celled green algae often grow, giving the sloth a rather greenish color that helps camouflage it.

Sloths eat only leaves, which are very abundant. They have no difficulty finding them, and there is no competition for them. Consequently, sloths have no need to hurry in order to secure food. These leaves are not very nutritious, however, and sloths have evolved to economize in the use of food energy by moving slowly. They also save food energy by allowing their body temperature to fluctuate, whereas most mammals expend a great deal of food energy maintaining a constant body temperature. In their warm habitat there is little risk of sloths being too cold, and they do not exercise enough to feel hot.

Monkeys are no less adapted to life in the trees, but theirs is an active life. They are much more selective in the food they eat, which means they must search for the items they prefer. They are highly social—unlike sloths, which are solitary—and they are also agile climbers.

Many species of American monkeys have prehensile tails, which can grip branches like an extra hand, making them even more agile. They can hang by their tails to reach for food, for example. No Old World (African or Asian) monkey has a prehensile tail. Despite this, the monkeys of Africa and Asia are no less agile than American monkeys.

APES

As well as monkeys, another group of primates inhabits the African and Asian forests: the apes. No ape has a tail.

Gibbons and the orangutan (the Asian apes) have very long, very strong arms and hands. They use these to travel by hanging below a branch and swinging from hand to hand. This is called brachiation; using this a gibbon (and perhaps an orangutan, too, although scientists do not know for sure) can move through the forest as quickly as a human walking on the ground.

There are about nine species of gibbons, forming the family Hylobatidae, or lesser apes. They are the smallest of the apes, measuring no more than about 2 feet (60 cm) long, and they feed on fruit, leaves, insects, and small vertebrate animals.

The orangutan (*Pongo pygmaeus*) can be up to 5 feet (1.5 m) tall. Its diet is mainly vegetarian, but it eats some animal food. Together with the African apes, the orangutan is placed in the family Pongidae, or great apes, although some scientists think the African apes, which are more closely related to humans than the orangutan, should be placed in the family Hominidae, comprising humans and their extinct ancestors.

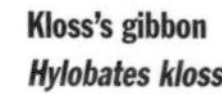

Kloss's gibbon
Hylobates klossi

APES ARE OUR CLOSE RELATIVES. Kloss's gibbon lives in the tropical rain forests of Sumatra, the orangutan in the forests of Sumatra and Borneo. The gorilla and the chimpanzee live in tropical Africa.

Gorilla
Gorilla gorilla

Chimpanzee
Pan troglodytes

Orangutan
Pongo pygmaeus

The African apes spend less time in the trees than the Asian apes, and adult male gorillas hardly ever climb trees because they are too big and heavy. Gorillas (*Gorilla gorilla*) are also members of the Pongidae family; they live in family groups and are very peaceful. They are strict vegetarians, so their food is abundant, and they are too big and strong to have enemies.

Also included in the Pongidae family are chimpanzees. The chimpanzee (*Pan troglodytes*) is about the same height as a gorilla—up to 5 feet (1.5 m) tall, but much more lightly built. The bonobo, or pygmy, chimpanzee (*Pan paniscus*) is not so tall.

All the apes stand upright occasionally, but only the Asian species practice brachiation. The African apes move by "knuckle walking," in which they close their hands so their knuckles make contact with the ground.

SPLENDORS OF ISOLATION

Madagascar is a large island in the Indian Ocean. It is separated from East Africa by the Mozambique Channel, which is 248 miles (399 km) wide at its narrowest point, and it has been isolated from the mainland for at least 50 million years. During that long period the animals of Madagascar have also been isolated from those on the mainland. Before it became separated, there were primates living throughout the warmer regions of the world, including Madagascar. The mammalian order Primates includes all monkeys and apes, including humans, together with their ancestors that are now extinct.

After the separation, those early primates died out in most places, their place being taken by monkeys and apes. The early primates survived in Madagascar, however, possibly because the separation left Madagascar with no native carnivores. Today they live mainly in the rain forests on the east side of Madagascar, where the rainfall is high because of the trade winds blowing across the Indian Ocean. Two lemurs, the brown lemur (*Lemur fulvus*) and the mongoose lemur (*L. mongoz*), are also found on some neighboring islands; they were almost certainly taken there by humans.

Altogether there are 28 species of lemurs, although some are not well known, and more might be discovered. They comprise five families: the mouse lemurs (Cheirogaleidae), lemurs (Lemuridae), sportive lemurs (Megaladapidae), indris and sifakas, also called the leaping lemurs (Indriidae), and the aye-aye (Daubentoniidae). Their brains are smaller than those of monkeys and apes, and their eyes are directed more to the sides. They have long, rather doglike muzzles, with a cleft upper lip and a moist tip (rhinarium) to the nose. Apart from the gentle lemurs (*Hapalemur* species), they rarely use their hands to manipulate food, although they will hold large food items while they eat them.

The biggest of them is the black-and-white ruffed lemur (*Varecia variegata variegata*), with the head and body measuring up to 22 inches (56 cm) in length; they are not large animals. The mouse lemurs are no more than about 5 inches (13 cm) long, not counting the tail, which is a little longer than the head and body.

All of these primates live in the trees. The only ones to travel regularly on the ground are the sifakas (*Propithecus* species) and the ring-tailed lemur (*Lemur catta*), which runs on all fours, holding its long, distinctively striped tail erect. The tail is sometimes used as a signal to warn off a rival. Both ring-tailed lemurs and sifakas are as much at home in the trees as they are on the ground.

Most of the Malagasy primates are social, but their social organization is very variable. (Malagasy means "of Madagascar" and is from the island's former name, the Malagasy Republic.) Some live in family groups of a male and female with their young, others in larger

LEMURS LIVE IN MADAGASCAR. They resemble the ancestors of modern monkeys and apes. Most of them inhabit the rain forest and spend almost all their time in the trees, some of them high in the forest canopy. All of them are vegetarians, feeding on fruit, leaves, flowers, and nectar.

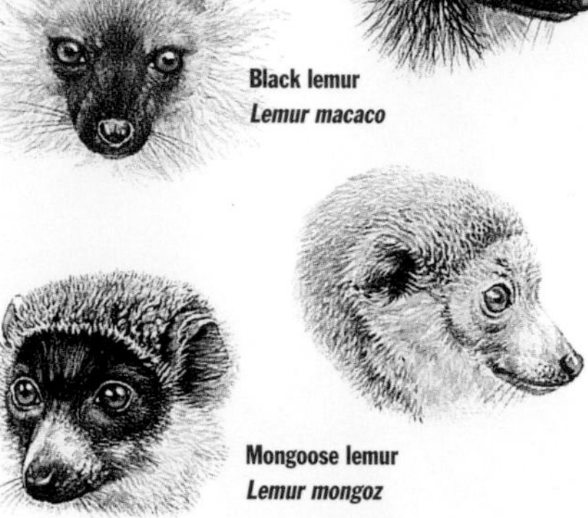

Black lemur
Lemur macaco

Mongoose lemur
Lemur mongoz

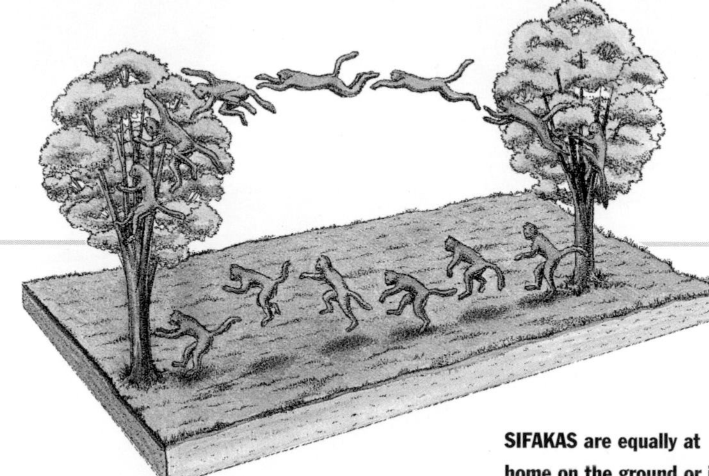

SIFAKAS are equally at home on the ground or in the trees. They can leap from tree to tree by jumping from an upright support, such as a tree trunk, and catching an upright branch or trunk of another tree. Alternatively, they can bound across the ground on their hind legs.

groups, and sportive lemurs (*Lepilemur* species) spend much of their time alone. Ring-tailed lemurs move around as groups of as few as five or as many as 30 individuals.

The Aye-Aye

Most lemurs are vegetarians. They eat fruit, leaves, and flowers. The mongoose lemur likes nectar. The aye-aye (*Daubentonis madagascariensis*) is more versatile. In addition to fruit and plant shoots it eats insect larvae.

The aye-aye is a curious animal, up to 18 inches (46 cm) long, with a tail up to 24 inches (60 cm) long, big, batlike ears, and huge incisor teeth that grow continuously. All its fingers and toes are long and spindly, but the third finger of its hand is the longest. The aye-aye searches for insect larvae by moving along a branch, tapping the wood with its long finger, and listening for changes in the sound. In this way it locates the tunnels drilled in the wood by wood-boring larvae. It tears away the bark with its long teeth, then uses its middle finger to probe for insects and extract them.

Woodpeckers find and extract insects using their bills and long tongues. There are no woodpeckers in Madagascar, which may be how the aye-aye came to evolve its long teeth and fingers. The aye-aye also uses its long finger to extract the pulp and juice from fruit or the contents from a bird's egg, and its teeth are strong enough to open a coconut.

THE NIGHT SHIFT

Monkeys and apes are active by day, but their ancestors slept by day and searched for food at night. Many of the Malagasy primates still live in this way, as do some groups of primates found in other parts of the world. Nocturnal mammals (those that are active at night) usually have very large eyes to collect as much light as possible.

Tarsiers (*Tarsius* species) live on the islands of the tropical Pacific from the Philippines to Indonesia. There are three species, all with heads and bodies 5 to 6 inches (13 to 15 cm) long and tails nearly twice that length. Their hind limbs are also about twice the length of their heads and bodies combined. They have nails on all their fingers and on all but their second and third toes. These have claws, which they use for grooming. Tarsiers' eyes are so big that there is not room for the muscles to turn them in their sockets. Instead, they have to turn their entire heads; like owls, they can turn them almost far enough to face directly backward.

Tarsiers are carnivorous. Individuals vary in their food preferences, but tarsiers as a whole will eat insects of all kinds, as well as scorpions, bats, lizards, birds, and even venomous snakes. They catch their prey by leaping and seizing it with their hands then killing it with bites.

Lorises live in the tropical forests of Asia, the slender loris (*Loris tardigradus*) in India and Sri Lanka, and the slow loris (*Nycticebus coucang*) in Southeast Asia. The golden potto (*Arctocebus calabarensis*), potto (*Perodicticus potto*), and bush babies are found in Africa. They range in combined head and body length from about 5 inches (13 cm) to 13 inches (33 cm). Like lemurs, they have a moist rhinarium (tip to the nose), and they rely more heavily than monkeys on their sense of smell.

Bush babies run and leap with enough agility to escape from most predators. Lorises and pottos move slowly along branches, without making a sound or disturbing the foliage, so they move almost invisibly through the forest. If they sense danger, they freeze and can remain completely motionless for hours. Only in a real emergency—on coming suddenly face to face with a large snake, for example—will they drop to the ground as a means of escaping.

All ten species of lorises, pottos, and bush babies, comprising the family Lorisidae, feed on insects, other small animals, fruit, and the gum from certain trees. They share their habitat with monkeys, but there is no competition between lorises and monkeys because monkeys are active by day, and lorises only at night.

Owls

Wherever small mammals are active at night, there will be owls to hunt them. Not all owls are exclusively nocturnal, but most are, and their bodies are adapted to hunting in darkness. They have extremely sensitive hearing, and the disk on the face of many species improves this further by collecting sound and focusing it onto their ears. They can detect and capture prey by sound alone, but if there is the slightest glimmer of light, they use that. Their eyes are huge, like those of nocturnal primates.

The owls that live in tropical forests are very similar in appearance to those of temperate regions. Often, they are the same species. The barn owl (*Tyto alba*), for example, occurs throughout most of the warmer regions of the world, including the whole of the United States (but not Canada) and in Europe south of Sweden, but it is not found over northern and central Asia.

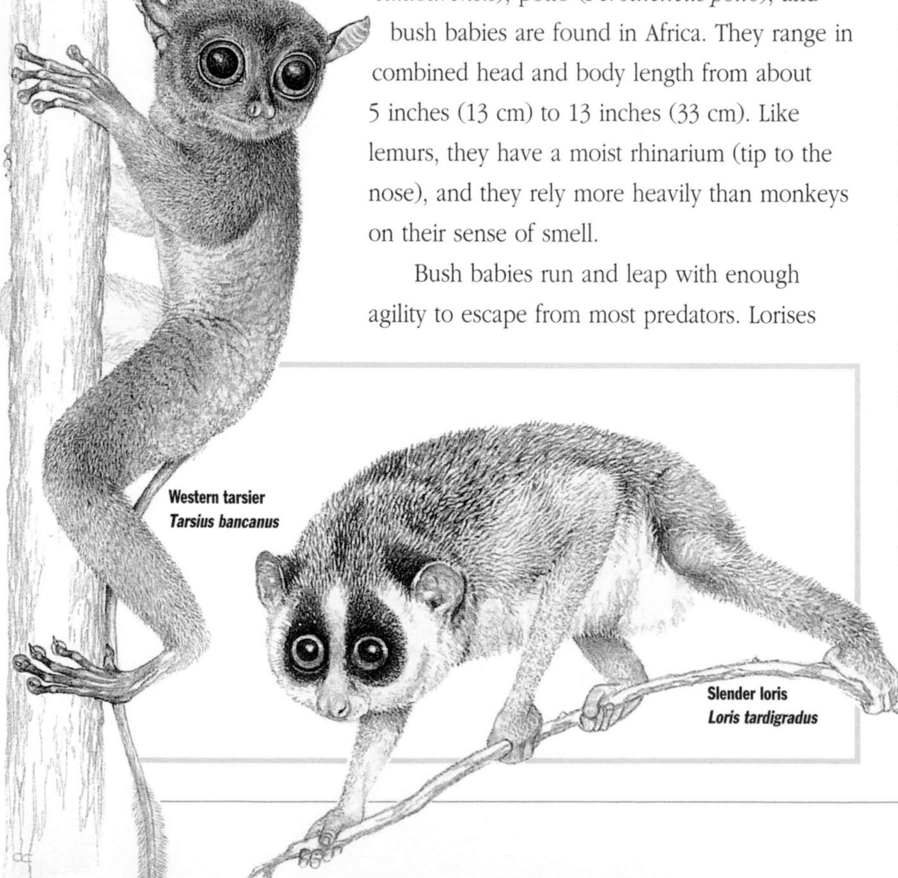

TARSIERS AND LORISES are small, tree-dwelling, nocturnal primates found in the tropical rain forests of Pacific islands, India, and Sri Lanka. Their large eyes help them see in very dim light, and their prominent ears are a sign that their hearing is acute. The claws on two of the toes of the tarsier are used for grooming.

Snakes

There are also snakes that are able to hunt in total darkness. Snakes are deaf, but some have organs that can detect differences in temperature of less than 0.002°F (0.001°C) between an object and its surroundings. These heat-sensitive organs are set in pits at the front of the head. They also allow the snake to detect the direction and distance of the prey.

Pythons and boas have heat-sensitive organs and hunt by night. The green tree python (*Chondropython viridis*) lives in the Australian tropical rain forest and is almost identical to the quite unrelated emerald tree boa (*Corallus caninus*) of South America—their facial pits are different, but apart from that it is difficult to distinguish one species from the other. Their similarity is the result of convergent evolution (see pages 30–31).

The green tree python is green only as an adult, however. Young ones are yellow or sometimes red. They become green when they are about two years old. The green color is caused by microscopic particles of a blue

PYTHONS AND BOAS can detect a difference of a fraction of a degree between the temperature of an object and that of its surroundings. This enables them to find prey at night. This is the green tree python *(Chondropython viridis)*, found in the tropical forests of Australia.

substance that lie beneath a layer of cells containing droplets of yellow oil. Very rarely, the coloration can go wrong. Individuals may lack the cells with the yellow color, in which case the snake is bright blue. Or they may lack the blue particles, in which case the snake remains yellow.

It is not only pythons and boas that possess pits with heat-sensitive organs. Pit vipers (family Crotalidae) also have them. The bushmaster (*Lachesis muta*), for example, is strictly nocturnal and hunts animals up to the size of small deer. The bushmaster can grow up to 11 feet (3.3 m) long; it lives in the rain forests of Central and South America.

Though not a pit viper, the gaboon viper (*Vipera gabonica*) of the African rain forests also hunts at night, mainly by lying in wait for prey on the forest floor. It is a big snake and can measure up to 6.5 feet (2 m) long.

MAMMALS ON THE FOREST FLOOR

"Jungle" is the almost impenetrable mass of vegetation that grows up alongside roads and railroad tracks in places where trees have been felled and the ground disturbed. Behind the jungle a tropical rain forest is fairly open. The shade on the floor is too deep for most plants, and it is not difficult to walk around. This means that large mammals can live deep in the forest, moving easily among the trees in their search for food.

These forest animals include elephants, the biggest of all land-dwelling mammals. Asian elephants (*Elephas maximus*) inhabit forests in the Indian subcontinent, southern Asia, and Indonesia. In Africa the forest elephant (*Loxodonta cyclotis*) also inhabits tropical forests.

In the forests elephants tend always to follow the same paths as they move around, and in this way they make "elephant roads." Elephants move a great deal because they need a large area in which to find food and water. An adult elephant needs to eat about 330 pounds (150 kg) of food and to drink about 20 gallons (91 liters) of water every day. In seasonal forests elephants will walk up to 20 miles (32 km) to feed on the fresh young plants that spring up after it has rained.

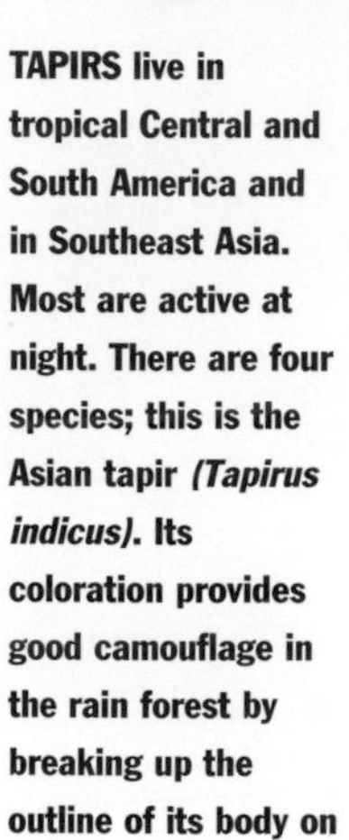

TAPIRS live in tropical Central and South America and in Southeast Asia. Most are active at night. There are four species; this is the Asian tapir *(Tapirus indicus)*. Its coloration provides good camouflage in the rain forest by breaking up the outline of its body on moonlit nights.

Rhinoceroses and Tapirs

Rhinoceroses and tapirs also live on the forest floor. Tapirs look as though they might be related to elephants and pigs, but in fact they are perissodactyls, hoofed animals (known as ungulates) that have an odd number of toes. The word *perissodactyl* comes from the Greek words for "uneven" (*perissos*) and "digit" (*daktulos*). Elephants belong to the order Proboscidea, and pigs are classified with cattle and sheep in the order Artiodactyla (even-toed ungulates).

Tapirs usually rest during the day. At night they emerge into forest clearings or visit the banks of rivers to eat and drink. The young shoots of plants are their favorite food, but tapirs will also eat leaves, small twigs, buds, or grass. They are big animals, measuring up to 8.5 feet (2.6 m) from nose to tail and weighing about 600 pounds (272 kg).

Rhinos are even bigger. The black rhinoceros (*Diceros bicornis*), of the forests and

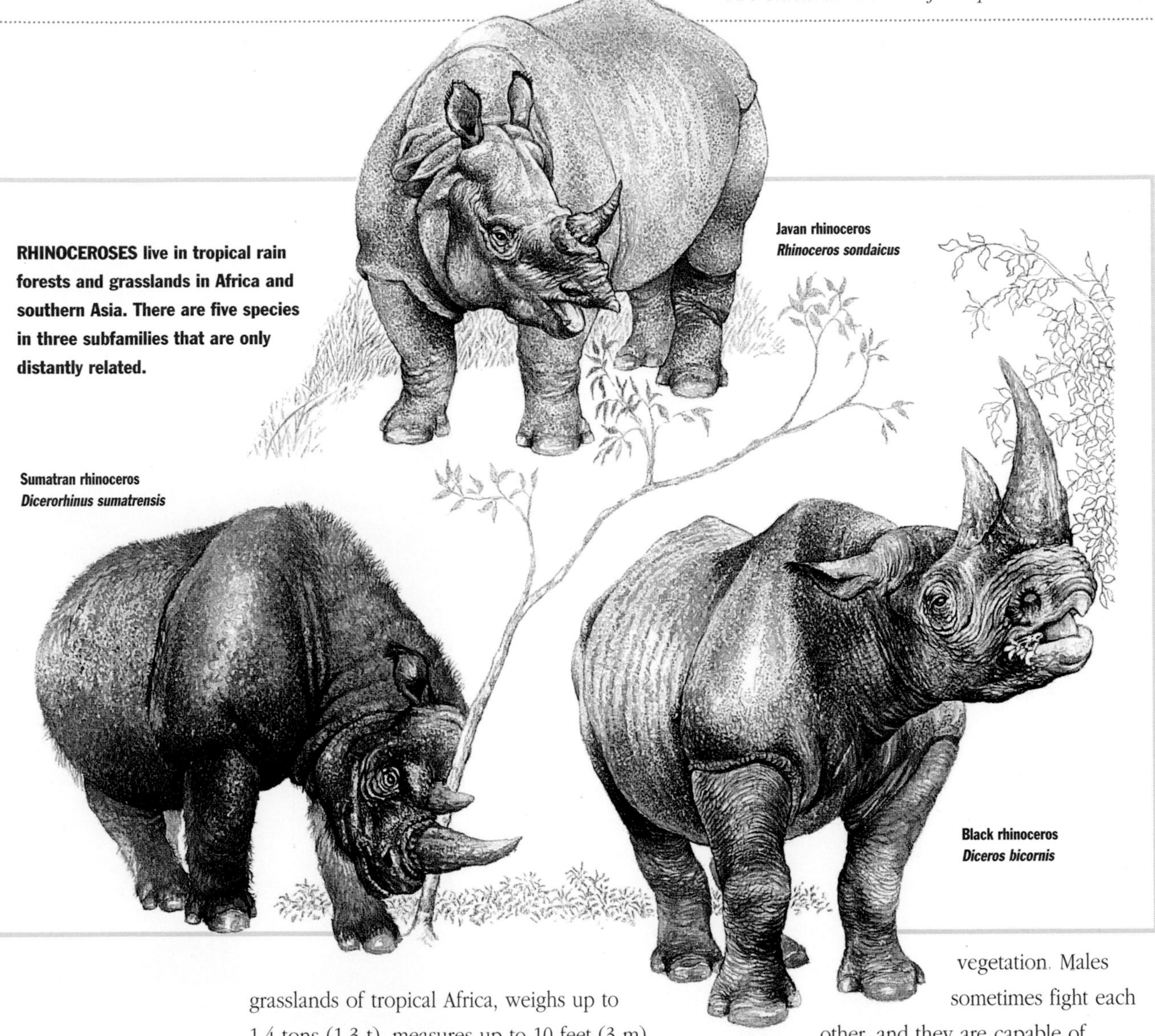

RHINOCEROSES live in tropical rain forests and grasslands in Africa and southern Asia. There are five species in three subfamilies that are only distantly related.

grasslands of tropical Africa, weighs up to 1.4 tons (1.3 t), measures up to 10 feet (3 m) from nose to tail, and stands up to 5 feet (1.5 m) tall at the shoulder. It has two horns. The front one is the bigger of them and is up to 4 feet (1.2 m) long. The one-horned Javan rhinoceros (*Rhinoceros sondaicus*) is slightly bigger, and the Sumatran rhinoceros (*Dicerorhinus sumatrensis*) is a little smaller.

Despite their size and fearsome appearance, with horns and skin so thick and folded that it looks like armor, rhinoceroses eat only plant material. They prefer leaves, but they are also able to feed on twigs and other fibrous vegetation. Males sometimes fight each other, and they are capable of inflicting terrible wounds, but rhinos tend to attack humans only if they are disturbed and feel threatened.

People have been hunting rhinos for centuries, mainly for their horns. Rhino horns are used to make highly prized dagger handles, and they are reputed to have many medicinal properties. The black and Sumatran rhinos have suffered most from the demand for horn. There is still a large population of black rhinos, but the Sumatran rhino is now very rare, and all the Asian species are in danger of extinction.

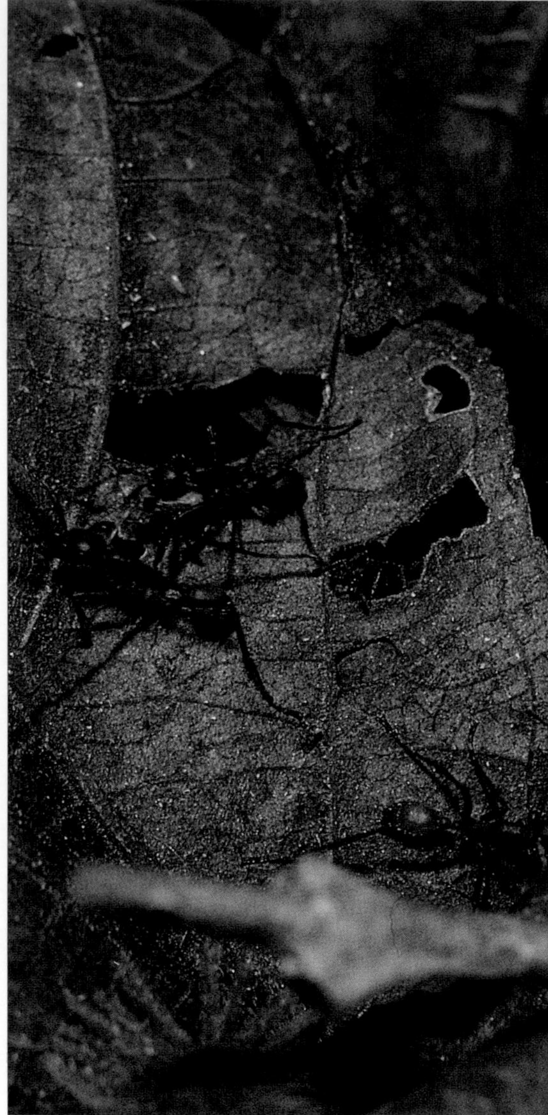

INSECTS ON THE FOREST FLOOR

Of all the thousands of animal species living in a tropical forest, the insects are by far the most numerous. Ants are the most versatile of any group of insects. All ants are highly social and live in colonies consisting of anything from a few thousand to several million individuals, and they have evolved ingenious ways of obtaining food.

Many are "farmers." In the tropical forests of Central and South America there are species belonging to the genus *Atta*. These are leafcutter, or parasol, ants: they cut pieces from the edges of leaves and carry them back to their nest, holding them above their heads like parasols. Back in the nest the leaves are chewed to make a pulp on which they grow the fungus that is their main food. Each *Atta* species cultivates its own species of fungus, and these fungi grow only in ant nests.

Other ants tend aphids—tiny, soft-bodied insects that feed on plant sap—in the same way that human farmers tend cattle. Some ant species even keep their aphids inside the ant nest and bring food to them. The method works because, although plant sap is rich in sugars, it contains little protein. To obtain the protein they need, aphids must consume a large amount of sap; this supplies them with far more sugar than they need or can digest. So they excrete the surplus sugar as a substance called honeydew, and it is honeydew that the ants eat. Ants protect their aphids and make sure they have ample food, and the aphids release honeydew when the ants stroke them in a certain way.

HONEYPOT ANTS are living larders. Like all ants, members of these species specialize to perform different tasks, and some become food stores. Other members of the colony feed them honeydew and nectar, which accumulates in their hugely distended abdomens. They will regurgitate it on demand to hungry ants that visit them.

Some "aphid farmers" go even further by storing honeydew. In a colony of honeypot ants (*Myrmecocystus* species) some individuals never leave the nest. Worker ants feed them honeydew and nectar, which accumulates in their abdomens until these are hugely distended—they become like honey pots. These "larders" will regurgitate sugar to any hungry worker ant that demands it.

Not all ants live in permanent nests. The subfamily Dorylinae contains about 200 species of insects known as army ants, or driver ants, which live in colonies of up to several million individuals. They are carnivores, moving in broad columns and devouring anything they encounter, including large animals. In many species the workers have no eyes, but are guarded by soldier ants with keen eyesight and fierce jaws. If these ants approach a house, the inhabitants leave until it has passed; the ants would eat any animal left inside. Instead of nests, these ants make temporary shelters, using their own bodies, with which they surround their queen.

ARMY ANTS do not build permanent nests. They are constantly on the move, marching along like an army—hence the name. These army ants have reached a gap—a yawning chasm—and are using their own bodies to make a bridge across it.

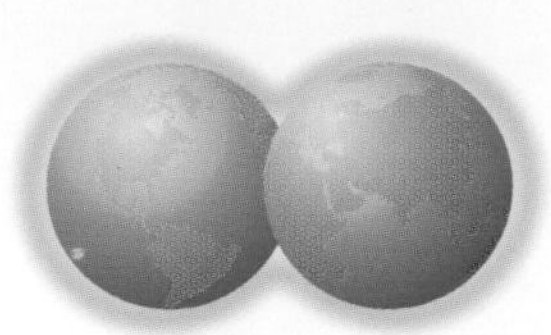

Survival of the Tropical Forests

Forests are disappearing throughout the tropics as trees are cleared away to provide land for farming. Removing trees and other plants destroys the habitat on which many animals depend. Some animals have become extinct, and others are endangered. The risk is now recognized, and governments are working with scientists to protect the most important parts of the tropical forests.

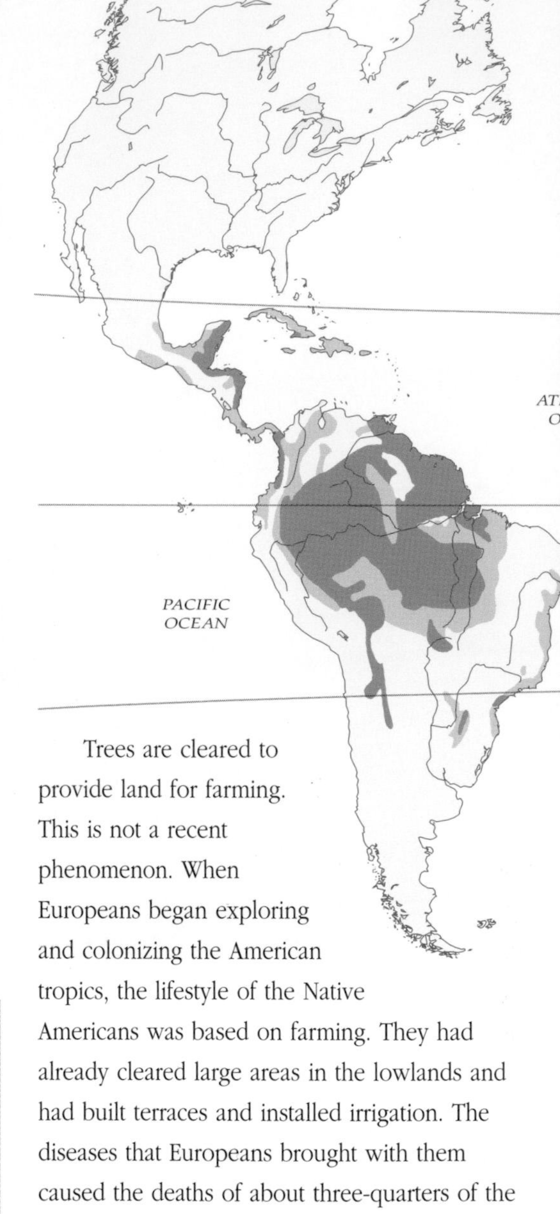

Between 1990 and 1995 a little more than 1 percent of the forests of Asia and about 0.6 percent of the forests of South America disappeared. The proportion is small, but the loss continues year after year, and checking it is very difficult.

Change in area of tropical forests 1990–1995

	%
Africa	–0.7
Asia	–1.1
Oceania	–0.1
North and Central America	–1.3
South America	–0.6

(Source: Food and Agriculture Organization, United Nations. Forest is defined as land where at least 20 percent of the area is covered by trees.)

Trees are cleared to provide land for farming. This is not a recent phenomenon. When Europeans began exploring and colonizing the American tropics, the lifestyle of the Native Americans was based on farming. They had already cleared large areas in the lowlands and had built terraces and installed irrigation. The diseases that Europeans brought with them caused the deaths of about three-quarters of the Native-American inhabitants. With too few people to work the land, by about 1650 agriculture had been abandoned, and before long the farms reverted to forest.

Today farmers are returning. What often happens is that a timber company makes a road

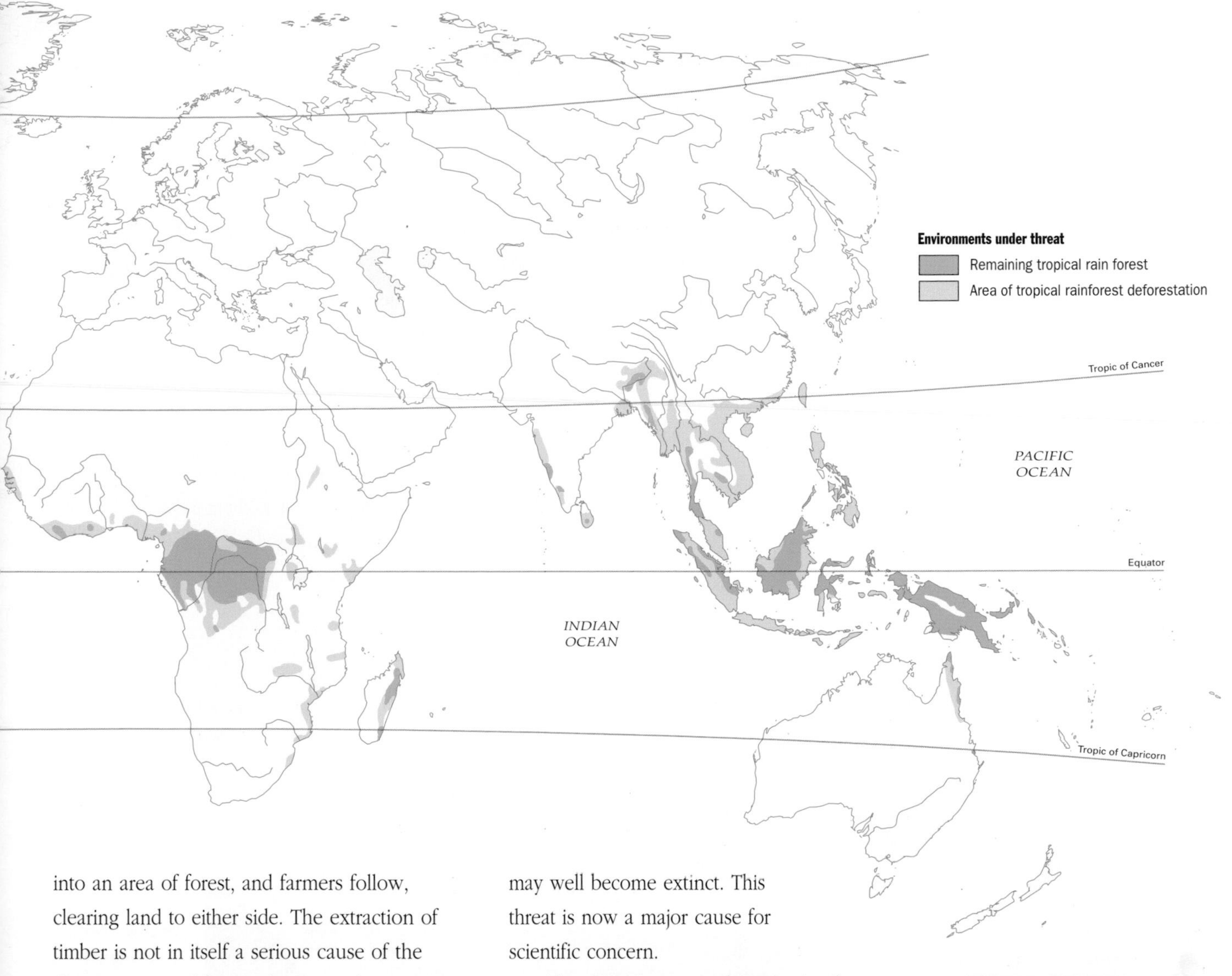

into an area of forest, and farmers follow, clearing land to either side. The extraction of timber is not in itself a serious cause of the disappearance of forests, but it can be a major indirect cause.

LOSS OF SPECIES

Tropical forests contain many different species. The richness varies from place to place. Not all tropical forests—even rain forests—support large varieties of species, but some do, and many of those species occur only locally. If the area of forest in which they live is cleared, the species may well become extinct. This threat is now a major cause for scientific concern.

The disappearance of species is often called a loss of biodiversity, but biodiversity, short for "biological diversity," is almost impossible to define; many scientists avoid using the term. What is certain, however, is that tropical forests contain many species that scientists have had no opportunity to study. They do not even have names. We know this because of the ease with which scientists can discover new species in the forests. Most of these are insects, but even more species of tiny inhabitants of the soils are yet to be identified.

FOREST CLEARANCE has affected every part of the tropics except for New Guinea. As the map shows, the remaining forests cover a large area, but a considerable area has been cleared to provide land for farming, especially in Southeast Asia and South America.

SOIL EROSION IN HAITI. Soil erosion on hillsides can be severe when forests are cleared and the land is poorly managed. Forest clearance and the growing of sugar cane *(below)* started a process of erosion in Haiti, eventually leaving the land incapable of sustaining agriculture of any kind.

Despite the losses, tropical forests still cover vast areas—987,000 square miles (2,556,000 sq. km) in Asia, 1,941,000 square miles (5,027,000 sq. km) in Africa, and 3,175,000 square miles (8,223,000 sq. km) in South America. Many parts of the forests are very remote and difficult to reach. They are so complex that studying them is a long, slow task and therefore an expensive one. Until scientists know more about the plants and animals of tropical forests and about how each species fits into the overall ecosystem, it will be impossible to say whether or not the loss of a particular species is important.

SOIL EROSION FROM HILLSIDES

During a rainstorm large raindrops fall with considerable force; in a forest the trees absorb most of their impact. When the rain strikes leaves and branches, it drips from them or runs in rivulets down the trunks, and it is moving slowly by the time it reaches the ground. There it soaks into the soil; much of it enters the roots of plants.

In areas where trees and other plants have been removed, there is nothing to break the fall of the rain. It hits the soil hard, packing surface

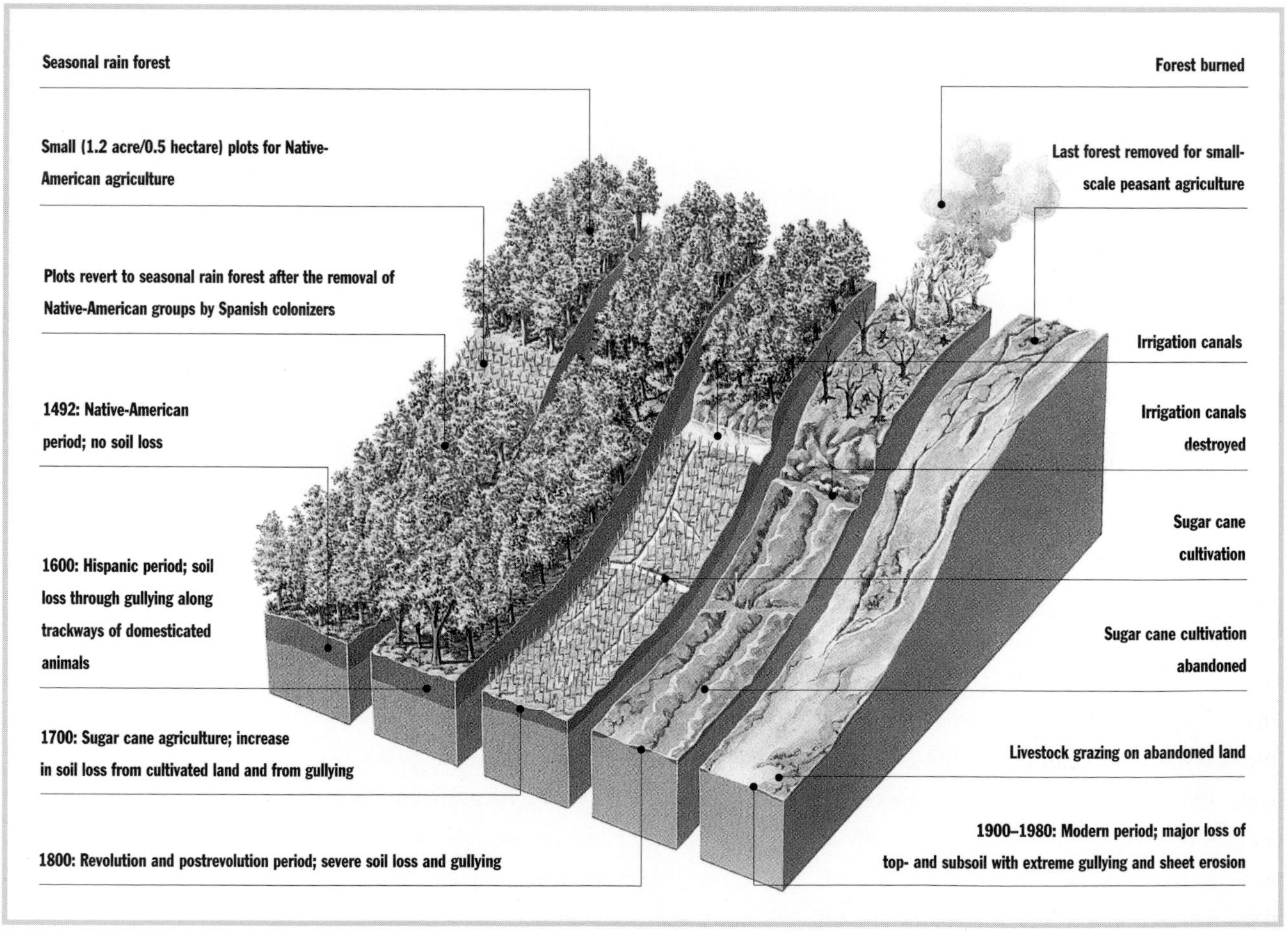

Seasonal rain forest
Small (1.2 acre/0.5 hectare) plots for Native-American agriculture
Plots revert to seasonal rain forest after the removal of Native-American groups by Spanish colonizers
1492: Native-American period; no soil loss
1600: Hispanic period; soil loss through gullying along trackways of domesticated animals
1700: Sugar cane agriculture; increase in soil loss from cultivated land and from gullying
1800: Revolution and postrevolution period; severe soil loss and gullying
Forest burned
Last forest removed for small-scale peasant agriculture
Irrigation canals
Irrigation canals destroyed
Sugar cane cultivation
Sugar cane cultivation abandoned
Livestock grazing on abandoned land
1900–1980: Modern period; major loss of top- and subsoil with extreme gullying and sheet erosion

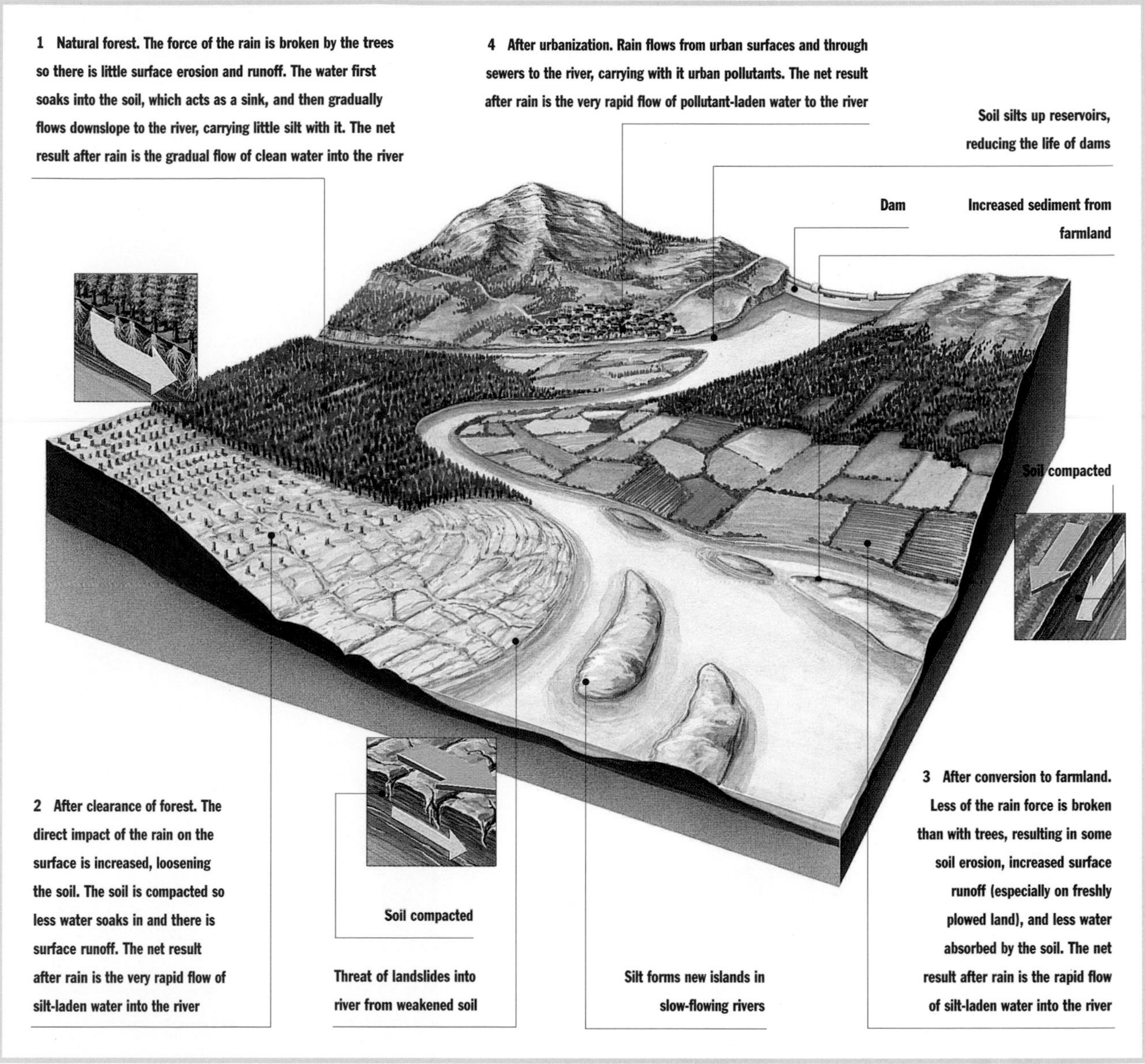

particles together into a thin but impermeable layer. Instead of soaking into the soil, most of the rain flows across its surface. It forms small rivers that carry away soil and form gullies. When the rain has ceased and the water has gone, some of the soil has been washed away, and the remaining soil is left dry—because little water has soaked into it. With each storm the damage increases, until eventually the land is useless for farming, the purpose for which the forest was removed in the first place.

Water flows downhill, of course, and the steeper the slope, the faster it flows. The faster the water flows, the more soil particles are transported, which is why rivers look cloudy and brown after heavy rain. For this reason there is a much greater risk of soil erosion on a hillside than there is on level ground. In many parts of

DEFORESTATION OF WATERSHEDS. Forests protect the soil by reducing the force with which raindrops strike the ground and by binding together soil particles. Careful farming techniques can avoid the risk of soil erosion and improve the soil.

the tropics, especially in Nepal and Haiti, the clearance of forests from hillsides has caused very severe erosion. The damage can be repaired, but recovery is slow, and the necessary measures are expensive.

THE NEED FOR TIMBER AND LAND

Timber has many uses. At one time large amounts were used to make railroad ties. The pit props used to support the roof of galleries in mines were made from timber, which was preferred to steel because it creaks loudly before it breaks, giving miners time to escape before the roof falls. The roofs of most houses have wooden frames and rafters, and many houses are built entirely on timber frames. Wood is used for paneling, many solid boards are made from

PRINCIPAL FOREST PRODUCTS. Most wood from tropical forests is burned as fuel or made into charcoal, mostly within the country that produced it. Almost all paper and pulp is produced from plantation forests in temperate countries, as is most of the sawnwood and wood used to make panels.

ROUNDWOOD
Fuelwood and charcoal
256
1,377
1,101
309
Industrial roundwood
Million cubic meters

PROCESSED WOOD
Sawnwood
359
87
16
93
Wood-based panels
Million cubic meters

PAPER PRODUCTS
Pulp for paper
120
14
21
154
Paper and paperboard
Million tonnes

Raised blocks signify developing countries

wood chips, and paper and cardboard are made from wood. This book is made from wood.

Collectively, all of these uses are counted as industrial. Many people suppose it is our demand for timber and wood products that causes the shrinking of tropical forests, but this is not the case. Of all the industrial wood being produced in the world in the 1990s, about three-quarters comes from temperate forest plantations

in the industrial countries of the Northern Hemisphere rather than tropical forests. In 1991, for example, the Food and Agriculture Organization of the United Nations recorded that Brazil, Argentina, Chile, South Africa, Malaysia, Indonesia, and the Philippines produced 5.05 million cubic feet (178.6 million cu. m) of industrial wood between them. In the same year the United States produced 11.6 million cubic feet (409.9 million cu. m), and European countries produced 8.04 million cubic feet (284 million cu. m).

Wood as Fuel

Some of the trees that are cut down in tropical forests are used industrially and to make wood articles, such as furniture, but these are intended primarily for domestic markets. They are not exported.

SLASH-AND-BURN FARMERS remove as much timber as they need, burn what remains, then sow their crops in the ashes. They continue farming the forest clearing until yields start falling, then they move to a new site. This clearing is in Brazil.

More than half of all the wood from tropical forests is used locally as fuel. Much of it is burned as wood to provide heat for cooking, fuel for trains, and for some industrial processes. The rest is heated slowly under airless conditions to convert it to charcoal. This burns at a higher temperature, so it is a fuel that can be used for such high-temperature operations as smelting, which separates metals from their ores.

Logging and timber production do not cause the disappearance of forests, however, because if the land is left alone, young trees grow up to replace those that have been removed, and the forest returns. Forest disappears only if the land on which it grows is converted to other uses such as agriculture. In the late 1970s about 7,700 square miles (20,000 sq. km) of forest in Central and South America was cleared to provide land for cattle ranching, sometimes with the encouragement of governments that favored the development of remote parts of their countries.

Slash-and-Burn Farming

A very common traditional method of farming is called slash-and-burn. Trees are felled in a particular area. Such wood as people need for building and making wooden articles is removed, and everything else is burned, including the small trees and other plants. This leaves the ground fertile, because its surface lies beneath a thick layer of wood ash containing plant nutrients. Crops are sown in the ashes.

At first crops thrive, and yields are good, but no nutrient is returned to the soil, and its fertility declines. After a few years yields fall and unwanted plants—weeds—choke the crops. The farmers then abandon the plot and start work on a fresh area of land elsewhere, repeating the whole process.

Provided the land is left long enough for the forest to regenerate, slash-and-burn farming does little harm, but this rarely happens because the time needed for the regeneration of tropical forest is 80 to 100 years. Suppose, for example, that a family needs about 5 acres (2 hectares) of land to feed itself, and that the land can be worked for only five years before being abandoned. If the forest takes 100 years to regenerate, this means that it will be 100 years before the family is able to return to the original plot. In the meantime it will have farmed a further 20 plots of 5 acres (2 hectares): a total of 100 acres (40 hectares). There is just not enough land to feed all the people who depend on it.

Slash-and-burn farmers lack the money to improve their farming by buying better seed, fertilizer, and tools, and they have no security of tenure. Lack of cash and security means they have little opportunity to cultivate forest trees with food crops between them—a method called alley-cropping—which preserves the forest.

SLASH-AND-BURN FARMING once did little harm to the forests, since human populations were low. Now it is a major cause of forest clearance because it requires a very large area to produce the amount of food needed by the much bigger communities dependent on it, and competition for land makes it impossible to allow sufficient time for the forest to regenerate.

THE FUTURE OF THE FORESTS

Improvements are being made, and ways are being developed to allow local people to earn a living without clearing the forest. "Eco-tourism" can be profitable. People from industrialized countries are willing to pay to visit tropical forests, which means they want accommodation, food, guides, and gifts to take home.

Protecting the forests is easier once plantation forests are established on land from which the

original forest has been cleared. Plantations supply lumber, can often be combined with crop-growing, and also provide employment. Their value is now recognized, and their total area is increasing. In India, for example, there were 73,000 square miles (189,000 sq. km) of plantation by 1992, and about 6,500 square miles (17,000 sq. km) of new land was being planted every year. Brazil had 27,000 square miles (70,000 sq. km) of plantation, and the area was increasing by about 770 square miles (2,000 sq. km) a year. Indonesia had about 34,000 square miles (87,500 sq. km) of plantation.

It is not possible to protect the entire area of tropical forest. People must be allowed to develop the resources in their own countries so forest must be cleared in some areas to provide agricultural land and, in some cases, to allow access to valuable mineral reserves. What should be possible, however, is the avoidance of waste. Plantation forests can supply lumber more profitably than natural forest, and with more efficient farming methods more food can be grown on a smaller area of land. Natural forests can then be used for scientific research, tourism, and the harvesting of some products, such as certain fruits, that are not easy to grow on farms.

In this way substantial areas of each type of forest will survive. If the forests survive, so will the small plants and animals that inhabit them.

Glossary

alga A simple green plant that lacks true leaves, stem, and root. Many algae are single-celled; some are multicelled. Seaweeds are algae.

alley-cropping A farming method in which food crops are grown on strips between rows of trees.

amphibian A vertebrate animal of the class Amphibia. The young develop in water, although the adults may live on land. Frogs, toads, newts, and salamanders are amphibians.

anastomosis The growing together and merging of the branches or roots of a plant.

bacteria Microscopic organisms, most of which are single-celled, that are found in air, water, and soil everywhere. Different types vary in shape and way of life.

biome A large region throughout which living conditions for plants and animals are broadly similar, so the region can be classified according to its vegetation type.

brachiation A method of movement in which an animal swings hand over hand along branches and from branch to branch. Gibbons move in this way.

broad-leaved Having leaves with wide surfaces rather than leaves in the shape of needles or scales.

buttress root A large, flattened root that grows out from a tree trunk some distance above the ground to provide added support. It is attached to the trunk all the way down to ground level and is triangular-shaped, like a buttress.

canopy The forest covering formed at the tops of trees by overlapping branches and leaves.

carnivore An animal that feeds exclusively on other animals.

chlorophyll The green pigment, found in most plants, that absorbs light energy. This is then used to drive the reactions of photosynthesis.

chloroplast A structure in the cells of green plants. It contains chlorophyll and is the site of photosynthesis. Chloroplasts have some DNA and produce some of their own proteins.

consumer An organism that is unable to manufacture its own food from simple ingredients but must obtain it by eating (consuming) other organisms.

continental drift The movement of continents over millions of years as the plates that together form the crust of the Earth move in relation to each other, carrying the continents with them.

convection Transfer of heat through a liquid or gas by the movement of the liquid or gas.

convergent evolution The appearance of similar features or behavior in unrelated species that is due to their adaptation to similar ways of life.

deciduous Seasonally shed, like the leaves of certain trees and the antlers of deer. The word is sometimes applied to structures, such as the scales of some fish, that are shed readily (although not seasonally).

dew point temperature The temperature at which water vapor condenses and liquid water evaporates. Dew point temperature varies according to the amount of water vapor present in the air (the humidity).

ecology The study of the relationships among living organisms in a defined area and between the organisms and the nonliving features of their surroundings.

ecosystem A community of living organisms and their nonliving environment within a defined area. This may be of any size. A forest may be studied as an ecosystem and so may a drop of water.

ecotourism A system that aims to exploit an area for tourism without destroying what attracted the tourists in the first place.

elfin woodland Woodland made up of dwarfed, gnarled trees, often covered with lichens, that grows near the tree line on tropical mountains.

emergent A tree that is taller than those around it, so its crown protrudes above the forest canopy.

epiphyll A plant that grows on the leaf of another plant.

epiphyte A plant that grows on the surface of another plant. An epiphyte relies on other plants only for physical support, not for nutrients.

eutrophic Highly enriched in nutrients.

fungus A soft-bodied organism that obtains nutrients by absorbing them from its surroundings. Fungi are neither plants nor animals but constitute a kingdom of their own, the Fungi.

glacier A layer of ice made by the compression of snow due to the weight of overlying snow that accumulates year after year. Most glaciers spread by flowing. A glacier covering a wide area is called an "ice sheet;" one confined by the sides of a valley is called a "valley glacier."

ground water Water below ground that fills all the spaces between soil particles, saturating the soil.

hapaxanthic Flowering only once during its lifetime, then dying.

hemiparasite 1 A plant parasite that grows from seeds which germinate in the soil. **2** A plant parasite that has chlorophyll and carries out photosynthesis but that augments its supply of nutrients by absorbing them from its host. **3** A plant parasite that has chlorophyll and carries out photosynthesis, using its host only for mechanical support.

herbivore An animal that feeds exclusively on plants.

illuviation The deposition of substances in a layer of soil, usually in a lower layer.

insectivore An animal that feeds mainly or exclusively on insects.

intertropical convergence The region close to the equator where the northeasterly and southeasterly trade winds converge, producing a belt of low surface pressure and high rainfall.

invertebrate An animal that does not have a backbone.

jungle Dense, scrublike vegetation that develops where tropical forest has been disturbed—beside roads, for example.

laterite A product of the weathering of some soils in a humid tropical climate. When exposed to air, it can form solid, impermeable masses.

lek An area on which the male of some species performs a display intended to attract a female. Females pass the leks and choose the male that most impresses them for mating.

liane Any climbing plant that hangs freely from a tree or other support.

lichen A plantlike organism consisting of a fungus and either an alga or a cyanobacterium (a bacterium that carries out photosynthesis) living in close association. The visible part of a lichen may be crustlike, scaly, leafy, or shrubby.

lung The organ of respiration in air-breathing vertebrates. In land-dwelling mollusks (snails and slugs), the part of the body involved in respiration.

mesophyll Tissue that lies between epidermal ("skin") layers of a leaf. It is where photosynthesis takes place and starch is stored.

monsoon A seasonal change in wind direction caused by the large changes in temperature over land and sea in the subtropics and the consequent changes in the distribution of air pressure. In winter, air flowing from land to sea produces the dry winter monsoon. In summer, air flowing from sea to land brings the wet summer monsoon. The word is from the Arabic *mausim*, meaning "season."

montane Of mountainous regions.

omnivore An animal that eats food derived from both plants and animals.

parasite An organism that lives on the surface, or inside the body, of another organism that is known as the host. The parasite is usually smaller than its host and gets food, shelter, or some other necessity from it. The effects of the parasite on its host may range from none at all to severe illness or even death.

phloem Tissue made up of channels through which nutrient substances are transported in solution to all parts of a plant.

photosynthesis The series of chemical reactions by which green plants manufacture sugars, obtaining hydrogen from water and carbon from carbon dioxide, the energy driving the reactions being provided by light that is absorbed by chlorophyll.

plane of the ecliptic An imaginary disk, the circumference of which is defined by the path traveled by the Earth in its orbit about the Sun.

plate tectonics The theory that the crust of the Earth is made up of a number of solid sections, called plates, that move in relation to each other. This explains continental drift and the spreading of sea floors.

predator An organism that gets food by consuming another organism. Most predators are animals that chase, overpower, and kill their prey, but insectivorous plants are also predators.

prehensile Able to grasp and hold on, like the tail of many New World monkeys.

producer An organism, such as a green plant, that assembles large, complex substances from simple ingredients. These may then be eaten by consumers. On land the principal producers are green plants and in water they are single-celled plants called phytoplankton.

rattan A climbing palm.

respiration 1 The oxidation of carbon to carbon dioxide in cells with the release of energy. **2** The action of breathing.

rhinarium The smooth, usually moist skin at the tip of the nose of many mammals.

slash-and-burn farming A system of cultivation in which an area of forest is cleared, its vegetation burned after any useful material has been removed, and seeds are sown in the ashes. Cropping continues for several years, until trees begin regenerating and yields decline. The farmers then move to another site and repeat the process, generally working a number of plots in rotation.

soil horizon An approximately horizontal soil layer that can be distinguished from the layers above and below it.

stilt root A root that grows out from the main trunk of a tree some distance above ground level and extends outward, entering the ground some distance from the trunk. It helps support a tree with shallow roots.

trade winds Prevailing winds that blow very regularly on either side of the equator, from the northeast in the Northern Hemisphere and the southeast in the Southern.

transpiration The loss of water vapor through pores, called stomata in the leaves or lenticels in the stems, of green plants.

tree line The climatic limit beyond which trees are unable to grow.

tropics Those parts of the world that lie between latitudes 23°30'N and 23°30'S. These latitudes mark the boundaries of the region within which the Sun is directly overhead at noon on at least one day each year. The Tropic of Cancer is to the north of the equator and the Tropic of Capricorn to the south.

understory The smaller trees that grow beneath the canopy of the major forest trees.

vertebrate An animal that has a backbone. Vertebrates also have a bony skull containing the brain and a skeleton made from bone or cartilage. Fish, amphibians, reptiles, birds, and mammals are vertebrates.

water table The uppermost margin of the ground water, below which the soil is saturated and above which it is not, although it is wet.

xylem Tissue consisting of cells that form channels through which water entering through the roots is transported to all parts of a plant.

Further Reading

Basics of Environmental Science by Michael Allaby. Routledge.

Biology by Neil A. Campbell. The Benjamin/Cummings Publishing Co. Inc.

The Encyclopedia of Birds edited by Christopher M. Perrins and Alex L.A. Middleton. Facts on File.

The Encyclopedia of Insects edited by Christopher O'Toole. Facts on File.

The Encyclopedia of Mammals, edited by David Macdonald. Facts on File.

The Encyclopedia of Reptiles and Amphibians edited by Tim Halliday and Kraig Adler. Facts on File.

Flowering Plants of the World edited by V.H. Heywood. Oxford University Press, New York.

Green Planet edited by David M. Moore. Cambridge University Press.

The Hunters by Philip Whitfield. Simon and Schuster.

Hutchinson Encyclopedia of the Earth edited by Peter J. Smith. Hutchinson.

The Lie of the Land edited by K.J. Gregory. Oxford University Press, New York.

Longman Illustrated Animal Encyclopedia edited by Philip Whitfield. Guild Publishing.

The Oxford Encyclopedia of Trees of the World edited by Bayard Hora. Oxford University Press, New York.

Planet Earth: Cosmology, Geology, and the Evolution of Life and Environment by Cesare Emiliani. Cambridge University Press.

Snakes of the World by Chris Mattison. Blandford Press Ltd.

The Science of Ecology by Richard Brewer. Saunders College Publishing, Harcourt Brace College Publishers.

Web site:

Rain forests: Diversity and Destruction, with facts and figures, details of tropical rainforest wildlife, and links, is at: http://www.davesite.com/rainforests/

Photographic Acknowledgments

7 Jacana; **8** Gerald Cubitt; **12** Colin Hughes; **15** Waina Cheng/Oxford Scientific Films; **17** Michael Fogden; **18** Jacana; **21** Marion Morrison/South American Pictures; **23** Michael Fogden/Oxford Scientific Films; **24–25, 25** Robert & Linda Mitchell; **27** Ingo Gerlach/Okapia/Oxford Scientific Films; **28** Jacana; **36** Michael Fogden/Oxford Scientific Films; **43** Frithfoto; **46–47** G.I. Bernard/Natural History Photographic Agency; **52–53** Victor Englebert; **Cover pictures:** *top*: Fritz Prenzel/Bruce Coleman Limited; *bottom*: David Hughes/Bruce Coleman Limited; *globe motif*: Terra Forma™ Copyright© 1995–1997 Andromeda Interactive Ltd.

Set Index

Page numbers in *italics* refer to illustrations; volume numbers are in **bold**.

A

B

C

D

E

F

G

N

O

P

Q

R

S

T